# THE CHANNEL TUNNEL

## ASPECTS OF HEALTH AND SAFETY DURING CONSTRUCTION

*© Crown copyright 1996*
*Applications for reproduction*
*should be made to HMSO*
*First published 1996*

ISBN 0 7176 0906 5

## ACKNOWLEDGEMENTS

All illustrations are based upon reference material from Transmanche Link (TML).
All photographs are from QA Photos, Hythe, Kent.

# CONTENTS

# FOREWORD

This book describes the management of health and safety and the reduction of risk during the construction of the UK part of the Channel Tunnel, and the resulting initiatives taken by the contractors. The Channel Tunnel project was unique in the scale and complexity of its operations, and site health and safety issues were a major concern of both the contractors and the Health and Safety Executive (HSE) for the whole period (1987–1993).

The task of writing this publication, based on the work and contributions of many people in HSE, was carried out by Neil Murray, the Principal Inspector who led the group of field inspectors during the last two years of construction. He worked with his predecessor, Stewart Campbell, and Hilary Weston, one of the group inspectors. The result is a forthright account of the experiences, sometimes tragic, arising from one of the largest civil engineering projects ever undertaken.

There is no question that there were significant improvements in the management of health and safety, and in engineering controls, for tunnelling operations during the years of the project. Many of these practices and lessons have been taken to other sites by individual managers of the contracting companies and have greatly enhanced health and safety standards elsewhere.

HSE gratefully acknowledges the support given throughout the project by the Safety Authority, by our French counterparts, by the officers of Kent Police and Kent Fire Brigade and by the management and workforce of TML.

HSE would also like to record the contribution of Cedric Harrison, HM Senior Electrical Inspector who sadly died during the construction phase of the project.

Now it is important that the widest possible audience should benefit from the experience of the Channel Tunnel. I believe that this document will serve as an important contribution to improving standards of health and safety, not only in tunnelling, but in the construction industry in general – an industry which has long been recognised as one of the higher risk work sectors. The wide range of issues described in the following pages will add to our knowledge about the prevention of accidents and ill health. I recommend it to all who are involved in, and concerned about, the improvements in standards of health and safety in the construction industry.

**J S Oliver**
*Area Director*

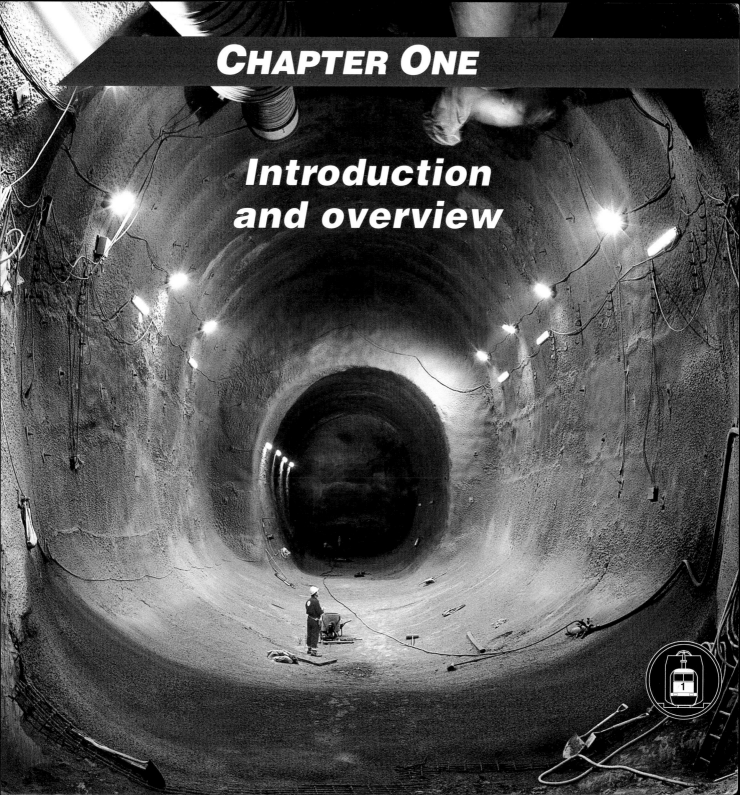

# CHAPTER ONE

## Introduction and overview

## Purpose of the book

1    This book aims to describe the health and safety issues – the problems encountered and the solutions found – which the Health and Safety Executive (HSE) considered significant during the construction of the UK part of the Channel Tunnel. It should be of value to everyone involved in future tunnelling projects including clients, designers, manufacturers of tunnelling plant and equipment, and contractors and should also be of interest to anyone involved in managing health and safety in major projects. It complements and adds to existing guidance on tunnelling and, while not seeking to deal with every aspect of tunnelling, identifies important health and safety principles in both management and practical techniques.

2    The construction of the Channel Tunnel, in itself a magnificent concept which had captured the imagination since at least Napoleonic times, was not only an outstanding civil engineering project, but also a remarkable mechanical and electrical engineering achievement. Work began before a fully worked-through design had been completed. Over a period of six years, while the design evolved, a consortium of major United Kingdom and French construction companies (Transmanche Link or TML*) constructed and, with a number of major sub-contractors, equipped a rail transport system under the sea between Britain and France. The UK arm of TML, formed from the UK contractors, was known as Translink Joint Venture (TLJV). The project is described in Chapter 2.

3    Many major technical, managerial and contractual problems had to be solved. Thousands of people were employed in an underground environment which could have become hostile at any time, with potential for an incident involving multiple casualties, for example from the outbreak of fire or from a transportation accident. Eight men employed on the UK side and two on the French side died in accidents during the construction of the tunnel, the greater part of which was built from the UK side.

4    During the first 18 months or so of construction work on the UK side, when site development was proceeding at a relatively steady pace, the accident rate was at least comparable with and (when reporting levels and the nature of the activity are taken into account) probably better than the rest of the construction industry. In many respects TLJV gave a lead to the rest of the industry on a wide range of health and safety issues, such as induction training and health screening, the use of risk assessment, and the involvement of trade union safety representatives.

* The ten companies forming TML were: Balfour Beatty Construction Ltd, Bougues SA, Costain Civil Engineering Ltd, Lyonnaise des Eaux-Dumez SA, Société Auxiliare d'Enterprises SA, Société Générale d'Enterprises SA, Spie Batignolles SA, Tarmac Construction Ltd, Taylor Woodrow Construction Holdings Ltd and Wimpey Major Projects Ltd.

5       However, HSE had already begun to arrange for a review of the effectiveness of health and safety management on the project when a steep rise in activity and production problems led to a significant deterioration in health and safety performance. This occurred as the four running tunnel boring machines began to operate. Half of the deaths on the UK side occurred during the space of a few months, before the full importance of the health and safety management problems had been properly understood and assessed, and appropriate solutions found and put into effect.

6       The deaths and other incidents and accidents resulted in a high level of media interest, coupled with political and public concern. HSE's inspectors carried out the planned review of health and safety management. That the situation was turned round by TLJV and a much better level of health and safety performance attained was an achievement reflecting credit on the contractors. It is particularly noteworthy that this was achieved in conjunction with greatly improved production and record tunnelling progress. Efficient production and improved health and safety went hand in hand.

7       The principal theme throughout this book is the importance of the management of health and safety. 'Management of health and safety' is understood here to embrace the planned and systematic approach to be adopted by organisations and managers with duties under health and safety law to protect those at risk from hazards at work. Because of the size, complexity and duration of the project it is not possible to describe fully the great efforts made by the contractors, but the key steps are outlined. Senior managers stressed the importance of ensuring high standards of health and safety on site and were supported by a dedicated team of site safety professionals and by an active trade union safety representative system. TLJV took a number of successful initiatives which constitute important positive lessons for the industry. However, as in any project, there were also lessons to be learned from failures. At the end of Chapters 3 to 12 there is a summary of the steps which can be taken to improve health and safety. Most of these have general application to the construction industry, though drawn from a tunnelling project.

8       The duration of the project (1987–1993) saw a number of HSE initiatives aimed both at industry in general and specifically at the construction industry which included the publication of a guidance booklet, HS(G)65 *Successful health and safety management* and the development of the Construction (Design and Management) Regulations 1994 and Approved Code of Practice. The guidance booklet only became available well into the life span of the project when TLJV was applying its principles, and the proposed Regulations were published for consultation towards the very end of construction. However, both of these identify the importance of making management arrangements and the successes and failings of the Channel Tunnel project with regard to health and safety which are described here underline their importance.

## The international legal framework and the role of HSE

9    The institutional and legal framework for the project is in certain respects unique. A binational Safety Authority (SA) reports to an Intergovernmental Commission (IGC) set up by the Treaty of Canterbury between the United Kingdom and France (see Appendix 1). A key function of the SA is to advise and assist the IGC on all matters concerning safety in the construction and operation of the tunnel.

10    During construction, the SA relied on the inspection and enforcement activities of HSE and its French counterparts. HSE's Safety Policy Division (SPD) acted as its link with the SA and the head of the Division was a member of the Authority. SPD co-ordinated HSE's input to the SA's working groups – health and safety, rescue and public safety, railway safety and dangerous goods. HSE also assisted the SA with technical assessments of 'avant projets', proposals for design and construction of various stages and aspects of the project, which were submitted by the designers as the project continued and had to be assessed with HSE's help and accepted by the SA against very short deadlines. The emergency authorities were also closely involved.

11    One of these avant projets, entitled 'Construction Methods and Safety', covered the arrangements for site safety before and after breakthrough in the tunnels. Broad agreement over construction safety was vital wherever actions on one side could have implications on the other, eg the use of the ventilation system.

12    The SA received regular reports on HSE's activities to enable it to monitor developments on site and encouraged, via its specialist working groups, co-operation between the national authorities over the development of standards and a common understanding of accident experience on both sides. HSE and its French counterparts recognised that there was much to be gained from the exchange of information and from liaison over approaches to health and safety, and, in addition to regular contact between inspectors at field level which increased significantly after breakthrough, staff from both countries met regularly through the SA and its working groups.

13    British health and safety law applied normally to the UK part of the operation and was enforced by HSE's inspectors. HSE has a statutory role to enforce the Health and Safety at Work etc Act 1974 (HSW Act) and other legal provisions for health and safety at work, and it does this by a number of means including advice, information, inspection, the issuing of notices and prosecution.

14      Inspectors from the Field Operations Division's Ashford Construction Group were responsible for inspecting the site, as well as other construction sites in Kent. They were supported by staff from throughout HSE, including specialist inspectors and scientists from the Field Consultant Group, the Employment Medical Advisory Service, the Railways and Mines Inspectorates, Technology Division and Research and Laboratory Services Division.

15      Examples of this joint approach included the work on fire risk assessment and prevention; the audit of TLJV's management of health and safety carried out in 1990 by HSE's Accident Prevention and Advisory Unit (APAU); and the better understanding of health issues as a result of HSE's work, eg on the treatment and prevention of cement dermatitis.

16      Inspectors dealt primarily with the contractors but also with other participants, in particular the French Labour Inspectorate, the Channel Tunnel Safety Authority and the emergency services. Inspectors had routine meetings with senior operational personnel from the fire, police and ambulance services and many of the issues described in Chapters 4 to 6 arose from these discussions. The contractors also met regularly with the emergency services and on numerous occasions there were joint meetings of all parties.

17      The inspectors who visited the Channel Tunnel project, and those who provided further expert help in HSE, were highly committed to seeking the establishment of the necessary health and safety standards in the project. Their work, in the same way as that of TLJV, was unique in many respects in furthering understanding of, and improvements in, conditions in tunnelling.

18      Agreement was reached between France and the UK in 1990 to site a temporary frontier at the point where the French and British tunnelling gangs met, to enable the majority to work under their own national legislation and safety practices with which they were most familiar. The permanent frontier was established in November 1992, when most construction work had been completed.

19      It has always been recognised that there are difficulties in comparing the accident records of the UK and France, but attempts have been made. The fact that there were eight fatal accidents on the UK side of the project and two on the French side at first sight appears to reflect badly on the UK part of the project. However, when it is considered that significantly more tunnelling (the UK contractors completed approximately 60% of the project) was undertaken on the UK side than on the French side and there were approximately twice as many UK employees of TML than there were French, the comparison becomes less striking.

20    Also, the accident reporting system on the two sides of the Channel is different. The UK requirement is that accidents which lead to more than three days off work are reported to HSE, whereas in France it is necessary to report over-one-day accidents to the Regional Accident Insurance Office. When the contractors attempted to prepare UK and French accident statistics on a common basis, these figures consistently showed a frequency rate and a severity rate on the French site at around twice that on the UK sites.

21    Towards the end of the project, TML organised two binational health and safety seminars and speakers stressed the value of developing common understanding. All those involved, the contractors, HSE and the French authorities, recognised that the most important conclusion for health and safety at work was that there were lessons to be learned from each side of the project.

*The UK terminal near Folkestone looking towards the entrance to the tunnels*

# CHAPTER TWO

## Description
## of the project

## The tunnels and terminals

22    The Channel Tunnel is a complex system which provides a railway between the UK and the Continent, much of which is undersea. The operational tunnels consist of two railway tunnels (running tunnels), each 7.6 m in diameter, carrying high speed mainline passenger and freight trains, together with special shuttle trains loaded with vehicles, their drivers and passengers between the terminals at Cheriton (near Folkestone) and Coquelles (near Calais). Between the running tunnels is a service tunnel 4.8 m in diameter (see Figure 1). Throughout the length of the tunnels, at approximately 375 m intervals, cross-passages have been constructed to link both running tunnels with the service tunnel. The cross-passages are 3.3 m in diameter and serve a number of purposes including emergency evacuation, maintenance access, the location of fixed equipment and the transfer of fresh air from the service tunnel to the running tunnels.

23    The tunnels run a total length of 53 km from Cheriton to Coquelles, 38 km of this being under the sea (see Figure 2). They follow, approximately, the line of the stratum of chalk marl (sometimes called 'the ideal tunnelling medium') which dips from the surface at a location inland of the coast on the UK side of the Channel and approaches close to the French coast, where it becomes folded. This necessitated the construction, not only of the marine tunnels from the closest points of approach of the two coastlines, at Dover and Calais, but also of land tunnels to link these to the terminals. Because of the sizeable area of land needed for the construction of the terminals (each of which includes a rail loop so that, when operational, the Eurotunnel shuttle trains could travel continuously between them), the UK terminal had to be sited at Cheriton rather than near Dover. This was the first piece of relatively flat ground along the chalk marl stratum, after it had passed at a depth of 45 m under the coastline at Shakespeare Cliff and had risen towards the surface under the North Downs.

24    The UK terminal at Cheriton is in an area of land about 2.5 km long and 900 m across its widest point with the M20 motorway forming its long southern boundary and the Downs its northern boundary. Because of the limitations of space, the UK terminal is much smaller than its French counterpart, which is about four times the area. Around Calais the land is much flatter and more was available for construction purposes so the terminal could be sited at Coquelles. This is within 3 km of the main tunnelling works at Sangatte, where the tunnel which passes about 30 m below the surface had to cross a more fractured and wetter stratum of upper chalk.

25    It was recognised that on the French side, this would result in the early part of the drive being subject to substantial water ingress and the French tunnel boring machines (TBMs) and

**Figure 1** Cross-section through tunnels and cross-passages

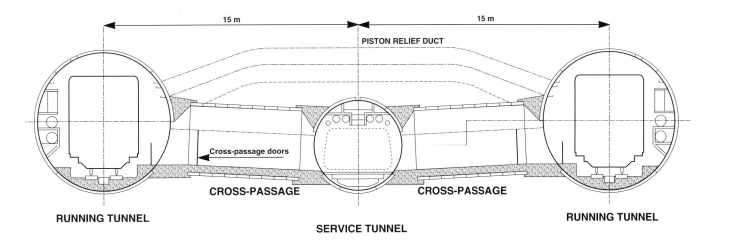

15 m

15 m

PISTON RELIEF DUCT

Cross-passage doors

CROSS-PASSAGE

CROSS-PASSAGE

RUNNING TUNNEL

SERVICE TUNNEL

RUNNING TUNNEL

the method of segment erection were designed to cope with this. The French TBMs were closed face machines using a Bentonite slurry method of spoil removal; the segments were fitted with a sealing strip in the segment factory and bolted into place underground. On the UK side, drier conditions were expected and the TBMs were open face machines with the solid spoil being removed by conveyor; the segments were locked in position by a key segment. When significant unpredicted water ingress occurred on the UK side, changes had to be made in the design of the TBMs (see Chapter 7).

26    The route from Cheriton to Shakespeare Cliff, Dover – the site of the main UK tunnelling works – goes under Castle Hill where the tunnels were driven by a method known as the New Austrian Tunnelling Method (NATM) through Holywell Coombe, which is about 900 m of cut and cover tunnels, and then through 8.4 km tunnels driven by TBMs to link with the seaward drives at Shakespeare Cliff. From Shakespeare Cliff, the route goes under the English Channel to Sangatte, a distance of 38 km driven by three TBMs from the UK side and three more from the French side. Finally, from a shaft at Sangatte, two TBMs worked to complete the last 3 km of the route to the French terminal site at Coquelles. The running tunnel machine was then turned round to cut the third tunnel from Coquelles to Sangatte.

27    Two undersea crossover chambers permit trains to be diverted from one of the two railway tunnels to the other in an emergency and facilitate maintenance of tunnels, track and equipment. The crossovers are situated about 7 km from the UK shore and 12 km from the French. The UK chamber is 163 m long, 21 m wide and 15 m high and is about 33 m below the sea bed. It was constructed using NATM.

28    In addition to the cross-passages, the running tunnels, every 250 m along their length, are connected by piston relief ducts which were driven over the service tunnel. Both the cross-passages and the piston relief ducts were excavated by hand tunnelling techniques. These ducts allow the substantial air pressure which builds up in front of the trains travelling through the tunnel to be relieved from one railway tunnel to the other. These ducts are 2 m in diameter and are critical to the economic operation of the project as they reduce the aerodynamic resistance to the movement of the high-speed trains.

29    There are two undersea pumping stations at low points of the tunnels built by the UK contractors, excavated on either side of, and below, the service tunnel and a further undersea pumping station in the French marine tunnels. Each of these pumping stations is about the size of a small underground railway station. Numerous other undersea and surface structures, such as electrical sub-stations and switch rooms, signalling rooms, ventilation and cooling buildings were also constructed.

**Figure 2** Tunnel undersea route

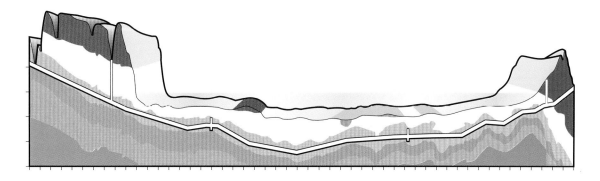

☐ White and grey chalk

▨ Chalk marl

▨ Gault clay

▨ Green sand

**The tunnelling sites**

30     UK tunnelling operations were based at Shakespeare Cliff, west of Dover, where both of the two earlier attempts in the 1880s and the 1970s had begun (see Appendix 1). The site was on two levels, the upper site on top of the cliffs being approximately 65 m above the sea. (These and following details are illustrated in Figure 3.) At the maximum extent of its development, the upper site included large numbers of offices, storage areas for materials and plant, canteens and welfare facilities, the communications and emergency control centre and the medical centre. The upper site was linked to the lower site at the foot of the cliffs by an inclined tunnel, driven in the 1970s attempt, which emerged on the lower site close to the portal of the British Rail tunnels under Shakespeare Cliff on the Folkestone to Dover line.

31     The lower site was developed from a platform originally created for the local railway company in 1843 by collapsing a section of the cliff using explosives. The Folkestone to Dover line still runs alongside the site and was used throughout the tunnel construction phase to bring the concrete lining segments to the site from the Isle of Grain segment factory.

32     The lower site was gradually extended by building a piled sea wall from the original lower site area towards Folkestone. The spoil from the tunnels was deposited within the lagoons created by the sea wall and gradually, as the spoil was consolidated and the ground levelled, the area was developed by TLJV for construction purposes. At its time of maximum development, large sections were set aside for segment storage and handling by Demag gantry cranes; there was also a concrete batching plant and associated material storage areas. In addition, the main locomotive marshalling areas and workshops were located on the lower site.

33     In the 1970s project, a 5 m diameter adit (adit A1) had been driven from the lower site down to the level of the main tunnels. Almost as soon as TLJV took over the site at the beginning of August 1987, work began to sink a 10 m diameter access shaft from the upper site to the line of the existing tunnels 110 m below and to construct a second adit from the lower site to the tunnel area. By the summer of 1988, both the shaft and the new adit A2 had been completed and from then on, although modifications took place, the means of access to the tunnel workings remained largely the same until it was changed to the portal on the UK terminal in 1992.

34     The shaft, equipped with two Alimak rack and pinion hoists, was the main means of personnel access; it was also used in conjunction with mobile cranes to lower equipment such as parts of the TBMs into the workings.

35 The 1970s tunnel from the upper site to the lower site was used by road vehicles, both passenger and goods, but was prohibited to pedestrians. The 1970s adit A1, although originally used for pedestrian access until the shaft was completed, and for a short time for a construction rail track until A2 was completed, was primarily used throughout most of the construction phase to house the main spoil conveyor from the bunker areas to the surface. Adit A2 when completed was used partly for the construction rail track and partly for road vehicle and pedestrian access, but as the tunnel system developed it was eventually taken over entirely by the construction railway with five tracks operating at the time of maximum activity. Road vehicles ceased to be used and personnel used the hoists in the shaft to get into the tunnels.

**The contract for installation of fixed equipment**

36 In addition to the tunnel and terminal works to create the permanent facilities, TML were also contracted to design and build:

(a)     the shuttle trains;

(b)     the rail track;

(c)     the electrical power supply and the overhead catenary system;

(d)     the signalling system;

(e)     the permanent tunnel draining, cooling and ventilation systems;

(f)     the service tunnel transportation system.

37 Most of the installation of the fixed equipment was carried out by major sub-contractors, commencing in stages in 1990 and 1991. Balfour Beatty Power Ltd were responsible for most of the electrical work; Laing Industrial Engineering and Construction Ltd carried out the installation of the pipework for cooling, fire water supply and pumping within the tunnel; and a consortium known as Channel Tunnel Trackwork Group laid the standard gauge rail track in the two running tunnels.

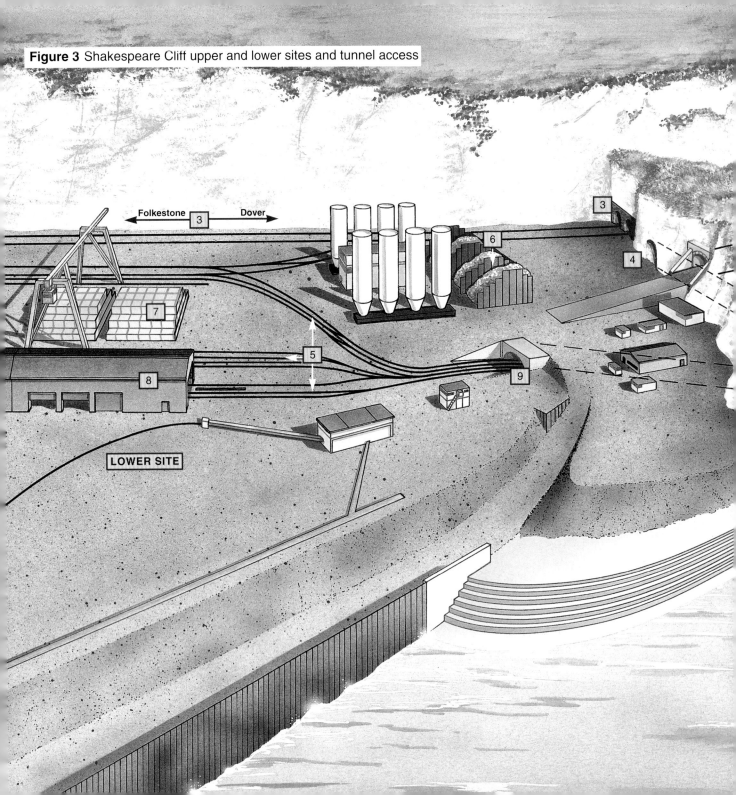

**Figure 3** Shakespeare Cliff upper and lower sites and tunnel access

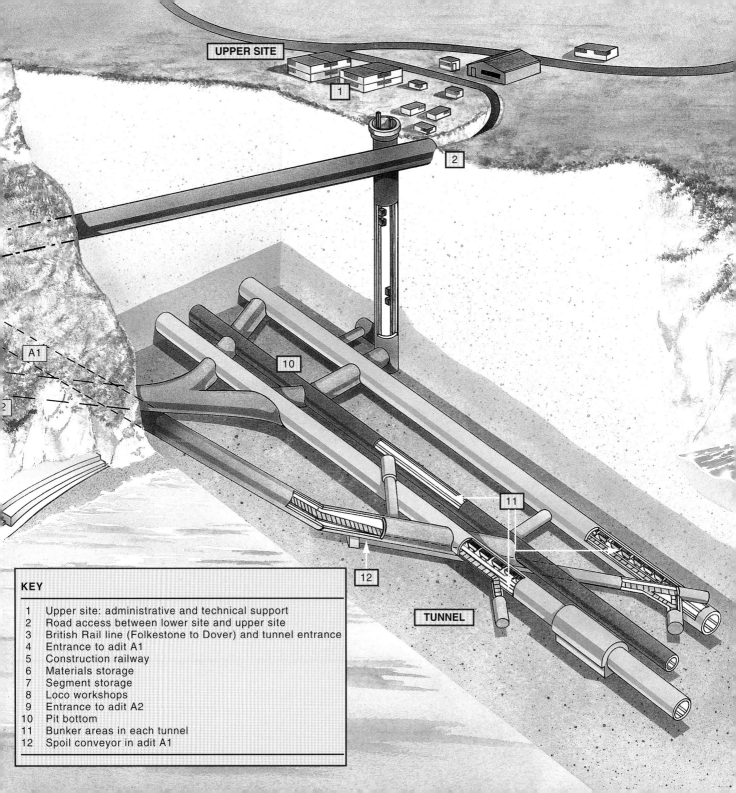

UPPER SITE

1

2

A1

2

10

11

12

TUNNEL

KEY

| | |
|---|---|
| 1 | Upper site: administrative and technical support |
| 2 | Road access between lower site and upper site |
| 3 | British Rail line (Folkestone to Dover) and tunnel entrance |
| 4 | Entrance to adit A1 |
| 5 | Construction railway |
| 6 | Materials storage |
| 7 | Segment storage |
| 8 | Loco workshops |
| 9 | Entrance to adit A2 |
| 10 | Pit bottom |
| 11 | Bunker areas in each tunnel |
| 12 | Spoil conveyor in adit A1 |

## Summary of tunnelling and fixed equipment progress

38    During the summer of 1987, the concrete plug at the end of the short section of marine service tunnel driven in the 1970s was removed and the old TBM cutting head was taken out. After TLJV took over the site at the beginning of August 1987, an erection chamber was constructed at the end of the tunnel and the marine service tunnel TBM, in dismantled form, was brought in via adit A1. It began its drive on schedule on 1 December 1987 but made very slow progress – by December the following year it had driven approximately 3.5 km. Throughout 1988, the area under Shakespeare Cliff was the scene of considerable development as the erection chambers and marshalling areas for first the land service tunnel then, in order, the marine and land running tunnels were excavated. The TBMs themselves began work one after the other throughout 1988 and 1989.

39    The land tunnels, which were all drives of 8.4 km, were completed in 1989 and 1990. Breakthrough in the marine service tunnel occurred on 1 December 1990 when the UK and French TBMs were halted and the final few metres were completed by hand. Breakthrough in the marine running tunnel north took place on 22 May 1991 and in the marine running tunnel south on 28 June 1991. In each of the three marine tunnel breakthroughs, the cutting head and shield of the UK TBM were buried and remain encased in concrete under or to the side of the line of the finished tunnel.

40    Installation of the fixed equipment (ie the electrical power supplies, overhead electrical catenary system, rail track, drainage, fire main and cooling systems), started with the power supplies and pipework in 1990; installation of the standard gauge rail track began in 1991. All of this work continued for a large part of the remainder of the project, with completion of the rail track installation in the UK project in December 1992 and the other work continuing until late 1993. Also, during 1992, commissioning of the fixed equipment began, and by the time TML handed over the whole site to Eurotunnel in December 1993, all of it was installed and the majority of it commissioned.

41    The numbers employed in the UK sites remained high for most of the project. Employment figures can be found in Appendix 3. An indication of the size of the operation was that in March 1990, over 8300 people were directly employed by TLJV in civil engineering in the UK. Gradually, tunnelling activities wound down and fixed equipment installation took over, so that by the first quarter of 1992, while there were still over 6800 people on site, over 2900 of these were sub-contractors. The proportion of sub-contractors to TLJV employees continued to rise as the project went on.

42     The following chapters describe the construction work in more detail and explain the importance of health and safety at work issues for these operations. Good health and safety standards contributed to the overall effective management of the project.

A running tunnel boring machine as it passes through
the UK undersea crossover cavern

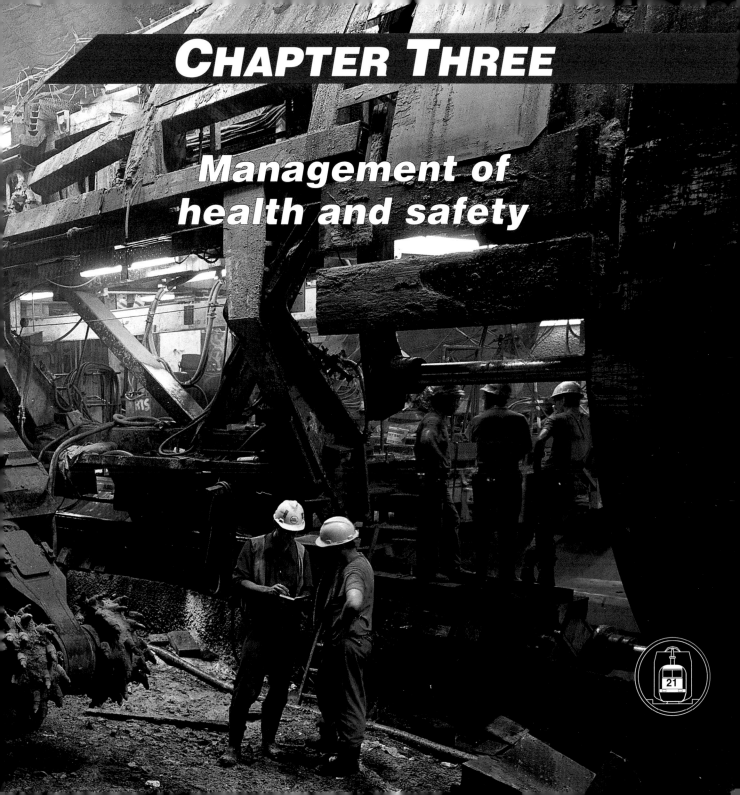

# CHAPTER THREE

## Management of health and safety

## Introduction

43     The central health and safety problem facing any major tunnelling project is that there are many areas and work activities which are remote or removed from direct management control; here, high risks may be met by individuals who are working in changing conditions. This chapter will examine the formal arrangements for the management of health and safety which were put in place by TLJV. The changes to these arrangements, as the project progressed, will be described chronologically to put them into context.

## Early planning and the use of risk assessments

44     TLJV and HSE began discussions in 1986, about one year before the start of activities on site. The meetings covered a wide range of health and safety issues, although the debate was dominated by the consideration of fire protection on TBMs (Chapter 4) and general tunnel fire safety (Chapter 5). Tunnelling activities using TBMs began on 1 December 1987. During the first 18 months of the project, the contractors took steps towards more effective management of health and safety, with a degree of innovation in their approach. For example, they provided a three-day induction training course for all new operatives; self-rescuers were used by all underground workers; the Trades Unions appointed safety representatives; and a safety committee was established early in the project.

45     However, as various health and safety problems began to arise, it was clear that the planning of health and safety needed to be improved. During 1988, HSE continued to press TLJV to adopt a more systematic approach. TLJV carried out a basic hazard assessment and engaged outside consultants (Bush and Rennie, part of the Ove Arup and Partners Group) to carry out a risk assessment. This work quantified the risks on site, eg fire risk, and prioritised them. The study concluded that for the Channel Tunnel project, the highest expected incidence rate would be from mechanical shock (falling or being struck), followed in order by asphyxiation, fire, electric shock and, finally, inundation (flooding).

46     The author of the report (Mr Douglas Parkes) concluded later in a magazine article that 'the assessment of technical as opposed to economic risk in the construction industry has been often neglected, and understated where consideration has been given to it' (UK Tunnelling, *New Civil Engineer Supplement*, September 1988). At that time, the use of technical risk assessment was indeed a new approach for most parts of the construction industry. HSE had already carried out a risk assessment on the use of mineral oils on TBMs (see Chapter 4) which was an important first step and underlined the importance of planning the control of risk from fire.

47    Great benefits for the project were derived from the planning for health and safety, and significant examples of this included the development of training programmes and emergency procedures, and the measures taken to protect against flooding and to control the outbreak of fire. However, in a number of areas effective planning did not appear to have taken place, eg design and site modifications to TBMs (Chapter 7), access arrangements (Chapter 8), and railway operations (Chapter 10). The importance of planning as a management function and the way it developed in this project following TLJV's introduction of a safety management system will be considered later in this chapter.

## Development of the health and safety policy

48    The health and safety policy which TLJV initially prepared was based largely upon that of one of its constituent contractors. It was revised at intervals to reflect several substantial changes which took place in the formal arrangements for the management of health and safety, including the development of detailed responsibilities and procedures, and the introduction of specific monitoring and auditing techniques.

## Description of management responsibilities

49    The revisions of the health and safety policy documents all contained descriptions of the responsibilities of line managers. However, inspectors found evidence at visits that line managers expected the Safety Department to deal with health and safety matters. Where such attitudes were found, inspectors took steps to inform the contractors. Later revisions of the health and safety policy placed responsibility more positively on line management and clarified the role of the Safety Department. The organisational diagram was also changed to show line management responsibilities.

## Arrangements and procedures for health and safety

50    Detailed procedures and responsibilities for specific tasks or processes were developed from the earliest parts of the project, and incorporated into the arrangements under the safety policy. As the project developed, many more separate management procedures were listed and incorporated into later policy documents, eg:

● Safety Training Manual;

● UK Construction Operating Procedures;

- TML Emergency Information Manual;

- TML Safety Management System Manual;

- TML Permit-to-work Co-ordination Strategy;

- TML Strategy for the Control of Substances Hazardous to Health;

- TML Strategy for Noise Control.

51    The identification of these procedures was itself a positive step in ensuring that those who were issued with the safety policy were aware of all the other supporting documents. With the other health and safety procedures, the safety policy acted as a framework and a reference point.

## Monitoring and auditing techniques

52    The early editions of the safety policy included general responsibilities for monitoring and auditing compliance with the policy, but the methodology for doing this was not explained. There is no legal requirement to conduct safety audits, and until 1993 (Management of Health and Safety at Work Regulations 1992) there was no requirement for formal monitoring arrangements. However, audits are highly recommended by HSE. TLJV did develop formal monitoring and auditing systems and these were described in later policies, eg:

(a)    interlocking tiered management and employee health and safety committees as a means of communication and consultation;

(b)    the investigation, reporting and following up of accidents with explicit remedial actions;

(c)    audit techniques including TLJV's numerical and qualitative audit systems;

(d)    method statements which set out management arrangements.

53    As the monitoring and auditing techniques were further developed, managers and safety department staff received training in them. The issue of training for managers is considered in paragraph 59.

54    One positive aspect of all revisions of the safety policy was the emphasis on pre-contract planning and, in particular, the use of hazard analysis for all new or changed activities. Although there were times when this was not done, the principle of pre-contract planning was set out in the safety policy.

**HSE's actions and site audit**

55    From the beginning of site operations, HSE carried out regular site inspections. A programme of visits was made on matters identified beforehand and unannounced site inspections were also carried out. HSE inspectors took enforcement action on a number of occasions, including institution of legal proceedings against the contractors following investigation of incidents where there had been no serious injury (some of this action and examples of HSE's site inspections are described in later chapters). During 1989, inspectors identified the need for TLJV to have a more structured approach to the management of health and safety to ensure that the aims of the safety policy were fulfilled. HSE field inspectors began to make arrangements for an audit of health and safety management on site to be carried out by the Accident Prevention Advisory Unit (APAU) of HSE.

56    Although HSE began planning for the audit in 1989, there were four fatal accidents on the project between October 1989 and May 1990. These accidents confirmed the grounds of HSE's concern, and resulted in a large increase in political and media interest in health and safety issues in the project. Nevertheless, HSE had already identified the need for action by TLJV and the audit carried out by APAU resulted in significant changes to TLJV's approach to management of health and safety.

57    Inspectors, trained in the use of a proprietary audit system, spent a number of days on site and the basic subjects examined were:

(a)    leadership and administration;

(b)    planned inspections;

(c)    accident and incident investigation and analysis;

(d)    emergency preparedness;

(e)    organisational rules;

(f)     personal protective equipment;

(g)     occupational health control;

(h)     engineering controls.

58     From the results of the audit, a series of recommendations was drawn up. These included the introduction of a safety management system, the development of health and safety inspections by management, management meetings at all levels at which health and safety was a significant part, and health and safety training of managers. There were also recommendations about monitoring and auditing techniques. TLJV accepted all of these and a number of organisational changes were made: in July 1990 Du Pont Safety Management Services were contracted to TLJV, and in September 1990 a new Director of Health and Safety was appointed.

## TLJV's contract with Du Pont Management Services

59     The first stage involved Du Pont carrying out an assessment of TML's existing management arrangements over about one month. At the second stage, their consultants provided training to TML line managers in integrating safety management into their overall workload. This dealt with issues such as leadership, training, investigating accidents and managing safety. Thirdly, managers were trained in the specific auditing techniques employed by Du Pont. Finally Du Pont looked at how the management systems for the fixed equipment sub-contractors were to be integrated. The evaluation of this work was carried out in three further stages over the following 16 months. Its overall value was to heighten significantly management awareness of health and safety issues.

## TLJV's safety management system

60     The 'Safety Management System' developed by TLJV in the autumn of 1990 was to be a practical programme of management action on health and safety issues. It consisted of a safety plan, training elements to support it and a programme for bringing it into effect. The plan itself consisted of six major elements:

(a)     A numerical audit system known as the Safety Performance Measuring Scheme (SPMS). This was an adapted audit system and underwent a number of revisions during its use. Audits using the system were carried out by a trained and appointed senior safety adviser with a small team to assist him. These were done on a monthly basis and were reviewed by the senior management health and safety committee.

(b)     Management safety walkabouts. These were designed so that senior managers toured specific work areas on a programmed basis solely to look at health and safety matters. The walkabouts also allowed senior managers to demonstrate concern about health and safety matters and to communicate the standards of safety performance which were required. They were intended to take place at least twice and no more than three times each month and were to last between 45 and 90 minutes.

(c)     Job cycle safety checks. These checks were carried out by line managers and were discussions about safety matters with the people doing the work. They were intended to be positive encounters to reinforce safe working practices, to be carried out at least once a week and to last between 45 and 60 minutes.

(d)     Safety check-lists. These were weekly check-lists of equipment and working areas completed by a supervisor or manager and copied upwards with comments about the action required. The check-lists were also seen by the director of the project concerned as well as the safety department.

(e)     Health and safety management committees. This tiered system of committees, beginning with departmental management groups and, at the top level, a site-wide senior management health and safety committee, were designed to ensure that each group was represented by at least one person in another group so that information could be passed through the management chain. The meetings followed a monthly cycle, with the supporting groups meeting in advance of the next reporting levels.

(f)     The existing Safety Representatives' Safety Committee. This was a communication system between appointed safety representatives and site management. The Committee met once a month and was attended by safety representatives and chaired by a TML manager.

61      To assist implementation of the safety plan, elements of safety training were also defined. This was a structured programme which took place in addition to other existing courses, and included field safety talks which were given each week by a supervisor or foreman to his team.

62      The most important benefit from the work by APAU and Du Pont was the increased awareness and knowledge of health and safety brought to all the working levels on the project. Du Pont consultants provided the detailed training to site managers by the early autumn of 1990. The interlocking safety committee structures were all operational by the early part of 1991 (the Safety Representative Safety Committee had been operational from early in the project). The last part of the Safety Management System to be adopted was the SPMS audit system.

63      However the difficulties of applying quite sophisticated management systems to an ever changing project were evident from time to time. It was never possible to quantify fully the benefits of the Safety Management System and there were times when elements of it clearly were not in use. For example, the investigation of the concrete bullet runaway (see Chapter 10) in June 1992 showed that the SPMS audits were not being used at that time by the underground operations department. Elements of the plan were not functioning on a number of other occasions, eg for UK crossover operations in March 1992; UK terminal operations in July 1992 (when on both occasions inspectors served Prohibition Notices on certain activities); and the problems relating to the 'overlap zone', also in July 1992 (see Chapter 12).

**APAU review of management of health and safety in 1992**

64      In September 1992, APAU was invited by the field inspectors to carry out a review of TLJV's progress in the management of occupational health and safety.  There was a meeting with TLJV at which HSE examined the management systems which had been introduced. The major area identified as requiring further action was that of planning. There were two levels to be considered:

(a)     planning at senior management level to control risks;

(b)     planning for the job involving hazard identification, risk assessment and risk control.

65      APAU advised that planning to control risks on a site level should involve the most senior management who should decide what the priority issues were, the overall action needed, and set objectives which then would become the plan for the site. This would ensure that individual elements of the safety plan (eg job cycle safety checks and SPMS) were tailored to meet objectives.

66      Planning for individual jobs had to be an active and not a reactive task. It was necessary to identify the hazards which could lead to loss and then to take steps to eliminate or control the risks which arose.

67      There was much that was positive about elements of the safety plan. For example, HSE inspectors attended several TLJV senior site management safety committees and found that safety audits, management safety walkabouts and field safety talks were all being discussed by both the main contractor and the sub-contractors. HSE inspectors also regularly attended the Safety Representatives' Safety Committee and were able to see the way in which information was provided at site level.

68    In addition, with the influx of a number of new managers during 1992 and early 1993 who were concerned with commissioning activities, TLJV carried out new or refresher training for managers on the Safety Management System. This consisted of a series of one-day seminars.

## Other management procedures

69    The Emergency Information Manual was one of the successful initiatives in controlling risk. This was a detailed, regularly updated document containing information and instructions to those responsible for dealing with emergencies. It set out procedures which ensured that certain specified actions were taken and named those who were to take the actions. On several occasions, when emergency action was required, those concerned were able to follow the procedures in the manual and prevent a serious outcome.

## Senior management meetings

70    Senior level meetings were held between HSE and TLJV during the project at which the Chief Executive of TML and senior area managers from HSE were present. They were on a regular (three- or six-monthly) basis and general management of health and safety matters were discussed. The meetings were able to identify a number of concerns on both sides and to discuss ways forward on health and safety management.

## Management of the commissioning process

71    Chapter 12 contains detailed information on the procedures used to manage the commissioning process. The use of work authorisation documents, test procedures and restricted zones all have application for civil engineering and mechanical and electrical activities and TLJV applied these control procedures during the latter part of the project.

## Summary of management of health and safety

- The most senior management need to prioritise health and safety issues, decide on the overall action and then set objectives from which a site health and safety plan can be drawn up. It is important that there are arrangements to monitor the achievement of the objectives in this plan and for reviewing it.

- Health and safety policies need to represent clearly the organisational responsibilities for line managers, provide specific guidance on monitoring and auditing techniques and refer to other documents where health and safety arrangements are described.

- All levels of personnel on site require training in health and safety as well as in monitoring and auditing techniques.

- Development of a safety management system plan which includes the elements of inspection, communication, monitoring and audit techniques would assist in controlling risk in tunnelling projects.

- Clear management arrangements for assessing the effect on health and safety of changes in production methods and procedures (including emergency procedures) are essential.

- Control techniques, including work authorisation, test procedures and restricted zones, are good control measures for those activities and areas where there are multiple hazards or where there is high risk.

- The safety representatives and safety committee system operated effectively.

*Miners positioning concrete tunnel lining segments*

*in the build area of a running tunnel boring machine*

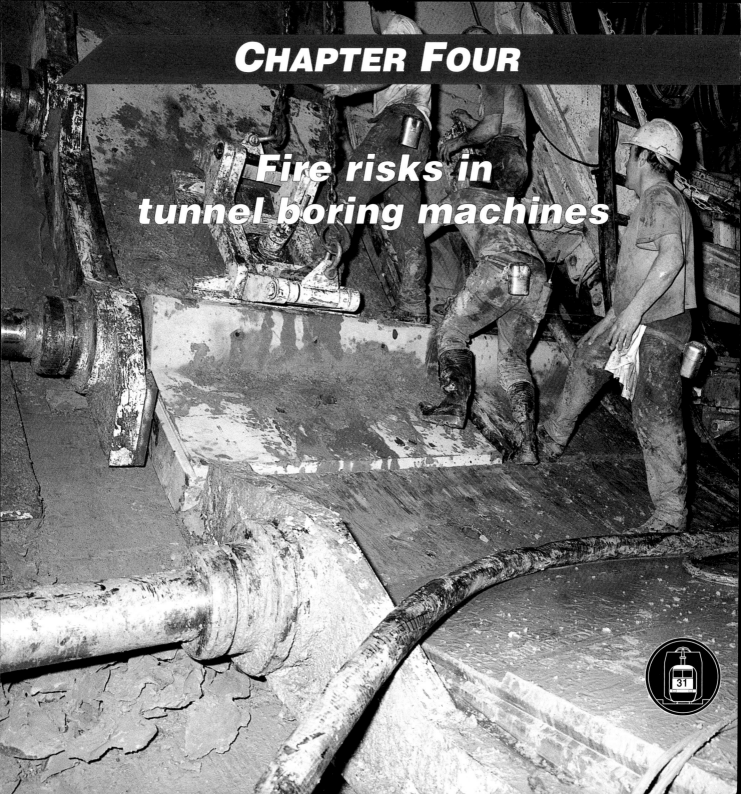

# CHAPTER FOUR

## Fire risks in tunnel boring machines

31

## Introduction

72     One of the main concerns during construction was that there could be an outbreak of fire involving the flammable oil used for the hydraulic power equipment of the TBMs. Each TBM carried about 9000 litres of mineral oil in its storage tank and pipework system. Considering the possibility of a fire occurring in conjunction with the exceptionally long travel distance for escape, HSE was concerned from the outset to ensure that TLJV adopted the appropriate standard of fire precautions and had workable emergency procedures. The precautions developed are applicable to all TBMs.

73     All tunnels are driven initially as blind headings, ie for the miners working at the face, there is only one way out, back through the tunnel. A substantial proportion of tunnels are driven as a single blind heading for their entire length, but there are exceptions to this where an underland tunnel has a number of access shafts along its length which can be used as means of escape. Even in these circumstances, the miners are still working in blind headings until the next access shaft is broken through. What set the Channel Tunnel, and in particular the marine service tunnel drive, apart from all previous UK tunnels was the varying, but always unusually great, length of the blind heading. As the two marine running tunnel drives progressed behind the service tunnel, there were alternative means of escape once these drives had been connected by cross-passages.

### The use of mineral oils on TBMs

74     At the start of the project, the current technology for providing hydraulic power to TBMs was by using mineral oil in the hydraulic system. Before construction work began on the Channel Tunnel, HSE set up a working group which drew together expertise in fire matters from across its entire organisation. In considering fire risk, the group identified the mineral oil to be used on the TBMs as the largest discrete source of fire loading in the blind heading. TBMs require hydraulic power for many purposes, including the hydraulic jacks and rams to propel the machine, steer it and hold it steady against flooding or sinking.

75     At an early stage, HSE pressed for the substitution of lower-fire-risk fluids, but two major arguments against this were advanced by the designers. The first was that if the TBM hydraulic system operating the systems to prevent flooding used a fire-reacting fluid, it would not be capable of withstanding water pressure if major inundation occurred at the face of the machine. The second was that, at that time, high-pressure hoses for use with such fluids had not been developed. Substitution would have necessitated a fundamental redesign of the TBM to incorporate unproven technology, and this would have been counter to assurances given by

Eurotunnel to both governments that the project would be undertaken using proven technology. HSE accepted these arguments and concentrated on the reduction of the risk from the use of mineral oil.

**Fire precautions on TBMs**

76    HSE wrote to TLJV in August 1987 setting out detailed fire precautions which were necessary on the marine service tunnel TBM. As well as technical specifications for various parts of the hydraulic system, HSE sought the provision of a fire suppression system for all TBMs, the requirements of which were that they should:

(a)    be activated automatically as well as manually from regular places of work or from the back of the TBM in accordance with written procedures;

(b)    use a fire-suppressant foam applied through nozzles in a pipe running along the top of the TBM which covered all areas where there were pressurised hydraulic circuits;

(c)    incorporate a sufficient reservoir of fire-suppressant foam to last 15 minutes;

(d)    include separate main and reserve foam pumps wired to different electrical circuits to ensure function in the event of a partial power loss;

(e)    include provision for giving audible warning of the imminent operation of the fire suppression system.

77    HSE served an Improvement Notice late in 1987 with regard to the marine service tunnel TBM (this was the first TBM brought into use) and TLJV provided a fire suppression system based on the principles outlined in the last paragraph by the early part of 1988. This also allowed for emergency shut-down of hydraulic pumps.

**HSE's fire risk assessment**

78    HSE's insistence that a fire suppression system should be provided was supported by a quantified risk assessment which the Technology Division of HSE carried out for the marine service tunnel TBM. The numerical conclusions were that the maximum risk of fatal injury (at a position 10 m from a fire) was approximately ten times the average risk of fatality in the construction industry in general. The risk decreased with initial distance from the fire, but nevertheless, computer modelling calculated that if a major fire did occur, the consequences

could well be severe, with people affected up to 1 km from the TBM. However, expert opinion was that, depending on the circumstances, conditions could become unsafe at distances greater than 1 km from the TBM, but that there should be enough time for safe evacuation of personnel from these areas.

79     The risk assessment recommended that a suitable fire-resisting fluid should be used. If that was not reasonably practicable, then a very high standard of precautionary measures, including fire precautions, should be adopted and rigorously maintained. TLJV were provided with a copy of the risk assessment and it was discussed in detail with them. Kent Fire Brigade were also actively involved in these discussions in their role of providing emergency action and rescue.

**Water spray barriers**

80     During 1988, the package of fire precautions was modified in the light of scientific research. The most significant development was that HSE carried out a number of fire trials using mineral oil in its test tunnel at its laboratory in Buxton, Derbyshire. The aim of these trials was to validate the theoretical figures used in the risk assessment but also, most importantly, the trials demonstrated that mineral oil fires in a tunnel environment would produce very high smoke temperatures (at worst around 140°C) very quickly (within one minute) with resultant high smoke velocities (up to 10 m per second). These conditions would threaten TBM escape procedures. The most effective ways of controlling hot smoke travelling away from the TBM were examined. Further research showed that a water spray barrier at the rear of the TBM would not only lower smoke temperatures to around 40°C but would assist with smoke dilution (so lowering pollutant concentrations) by actively mixing clean tunnel air with the smoke layer. HSE wrote to TLJV in 1989 indicating that a water spray barrier should be provided at the back of TBMs. Detailed features were:

(a)     The water spray barrier should be sited towards the rear of the machine at a position in the overlap/interface of the general tunnel ventilation duct and the TBM ventilation pick-up point. This position of the barrier was important to achieve the mixing of clean tunnel air with the smoke layer.

(b)     The water pipe should follow the profile of the tunnel roof and should stand off by approximately 150 mm.

(c)     The water spray should be arranged on the pipe to point inwards, that is towards the central point of the tunnel cross-section.

(d)    The nozzles should be arranged along the top quadrant.

(e)    The water spray barrier should operate at between 5 to 9 bar and be controlled by a clearly marked, quick-actioned handled valve.

(f)    Activation of the water spray barrier should divert the main tunnel ventilation air away from the sprayed water of the barrier. This would prevent the main tunnel ventilation air disturbing the barrier operation.

81    TLJV subsequently installed water spray barriers on all three marine TBMs.

82    It is essential to maintain fire suppression systems and water spray barriers. At several visits, inspectors found that foam tanks were very nearly empty or that the water spray barrier did not work properly. HSE reminded TLJV that a schedule of maintenance should be drawn up and that it is also important to test regularly that systems can be activated; these tests should be programmed into schedules.

**Escape and rescue**

83    The Buxton fire trials also concentrated attention on the problems of escape and rescue, in particular:

(a)    the means of ensuring escape from TBMs in the event of fire;

(b)    limiting the length of the blind heading.

84    Means of ensuring escape from the TBMs had also been considered in detail from the beginning of the project. HSE wrote to TLJV confirming that:

(a)    a clear passageway should be maintained throughout the whole length of the TBM;

(b)    at least one manriding vehicle capable of holding all crew and visitors present at the face should always be kept at the TBM;

(c)    the lengths of the blind headings should be kept to a minimum.

85    By 1989, TLJV had responded to HSE's concerns about rescue provision as follows:

(a)    Self-rescuers had been provided for every person below ground since the beginning of the project. These were carried by visitors as well as employees and had a duration of 90 minutes providing protection against carbon monoxide.

(b)    Special manriding trains were provided at the back of the TBMs. These were known as 'protected manriders' and carried compressed air equipment consisting of face masks connected to a bank of air cylinders via an air main fitted with a pressure reduction valve. The system had a duration of one hour and was capable of providing rescue for 25 people.

(c)    Breathing apparatus, in the form of chemical/oxygen sets, was provided for the locomotive drivers; these were stored in the driver's cab and had a 45 minute duration.

(d)    TLJV established an emergency response team to provide a round-the-clock service underground. Its role and activities were developed in co-operation with the emergency services, particularly Kent Fire Brigade. A rescue train equipped in a similar way to the protected manrider was provided for the use of the emergency teams.

(e)    Long-duration breathing apparatus oxygen sets with a 2 hour 30 minute duration were provided for use by TLJV rescue teams (these were also used by Kent Fire Brigade).

86    Training was provided in the use of respiratory protective equipment and exercises were held to test emergency procedures. During the project, a number of evacuation tests were carried out.

**Actions later in the project**

87    The Buxton fire trials and related research (see paragraph 127 and Appendix 2) also emphasised the need to control the length of the blind heading. HSE had concluded in 1988, based on the risk assessment, that the most important requirement was for rapid escape from the TBM and its immediate vicinity and that this would be a problem over any significant distance. However, HSE insisted, as the two marine running tunnels progressed in 1990, that TLJV ensure full fire separation in the cross-passages between the tunnels with structural fire separation at cross-passages and other inter-connecting ducts to limit the spread of smoke or hot gases. Access doors were to be provided which were available for escape or rescue. An Improvement Notice was eventually served on TLJV in June 1990 requiring speedy completion of separation work which had been proceeding, but too slowly and not to a reasonable

standard. This provided for earlier escape from a smoke-logged tunnel and reduced the length of the blind heading of the marine service tunnel.

**Summary of safety issues in the use of mineral oils on TBMs**

- A written risk assessment which includes fire is essential, carried out by the designers/manufacturers of TBMs.

- Mineral oils should be replaced by fire-resisting fluids unless it is not reasonably practicable to do so and/or there are other overriding safety factors such as prevention of flooding.

- If flammable oils are used, then the following help provide control in the event of fire:

  - a fire detection and suppression system designed for the TBM which will act directly on the hydraulic systems;

  - a water spray barrier.

- It is essential that these systems are properly maintained and regularly tested.

- Adequate escape and rescue facilities are necessary, including respiratory protective equipment and escape vehicles.

- It is important to reduce the length of blind headings by all reasonably practicable means.

The 11 000 V power cable drum on a tunnel boring machine

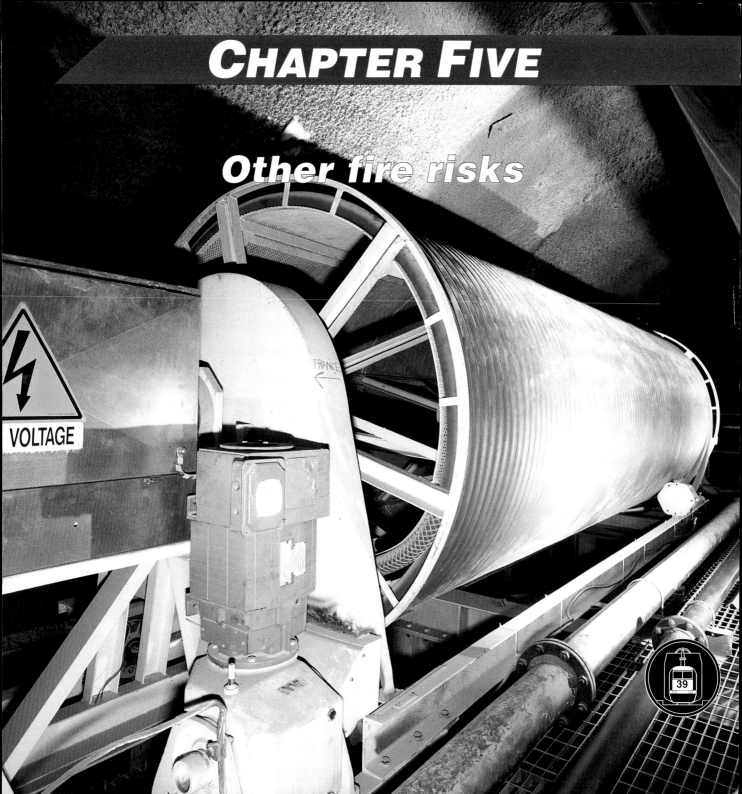

# CHAPTER FIVE

## Other fire risks

## Introduction

88    The consequences of a fire underground are universally recognised as being potentially very serious. Fires behave differently in a restricted tunnel environment from the way they do above ground, eg flame elongation along the tunnel roof – the way the flame spreads out – can be increased by a factor varying between five and tenfold. Also, the hot products of combustion (smoke and gases) remain within the tunnel, unless otherwise vented, leading to a substantial increase in the temperature and radiant heat effects.

89    Tunnelling presents special problems both in reducing the risk of fire, and the emergency actions to be taken in the event of a fire occurring. The principle of reducing the amount of flammable and combustible material (the fire loading) in a tunnel to reduce the risk of a fire, and its consequences, is well known. It was not easy to achieve this goal in a project as complex as the Channel Tunnel where work was going on at numerous locations, and conditions underground were changing rapidly. The reduction and control of fire loading can be achieved by:

(a)    planning the work;

(b)    assessing the equipment which has been selected (including its design) before it is used;

(c)    monitoring that the work methods and the plant continue to minimise fire risk.

### Compressed flammable gases

90    Flammable gases are used underground for a number of purposes, eg when building or modifying TBMs, repairing pipework, or when carrying out maintenance of static plant or mobile equipment which is permanently underground. It is essential that the use of compressed flammable gases is rigidly controlled. An incident occurred during maintenance work at Easter 1988 in the marine service tunnel when rolling stock which was being pushed by a locomotive near the TBM struck and ruptured a 47 kg propane cylinder which had been left on the trackside. A large cloud of propane vapour was released. Fortunately there was no ignition as it appears that the gas was dispersed by the tunnel ventilation system.

91    The investigation by HSE showed that the propane had been used in the tunnel for hot cutting work to carry out modifications to the marine service tunnel TBM. The permit system for flammable gases below ground had not been followed for eight days: the use and storage of gas cylinders were not controlled; there were accumulations of combustible material in the immediate vicinity; there was evidence of smoking; and lack of management control. TLJV

were subsequently prosecuted by HSE for failing to provide a safe system of work for the use of flammable gases during maintenance.

92 The general steps developed to control compressed gases included:

(a) Only small sets of oxy-acetylene gas equipment were permitted. These were supplied in capacities of 30 kg cylinders for oxygen and 13 kg cylinders for acetylene. The cylinders were secured in carrying frames.

(b) Hand-held extinguishers were provided fixed to each set.

(c) An employee was designated as a standby fireman to operate the extinguisher for small fires only.

(d) A certification system, known as the permit-to-burn certificate was used. The Control Centre of the project kept a computer record of all active permits (including the locations of intended use) so that adherence to procedures could be monitored.

93 Despite these steps, the nature of the work underground and the time delays in transporting equipment meant that the unauthorised use of gas-cutting equipment was on occasion discovered during routine inspections by management and safety representatives. The situation improved as the project went on.

**Electrical equipment**

94 Electrical equipment formed part of the overall fire load as well as a source of ignition. A number of fires occurred on the UK side in oil-filled transformers with a particularly serious incident occurring in one of the underground battery charging areas.

95 On 26 September 1990, a serious fire occurred in the battery charging station located at the marshalling area adjacent to the marine running tunnel north. It started with an internal explosion and fire in a charging unit because a traction battery on charge had been connected wrongly, leading to reversed polarity. The fire spread to 16 adjacent charging units which were completely destroyed. There was a large amount of smoke emission in the area and the tunnel was evacuated in the vicinity of the charging station.

96    HSE's investigation revealed that the system for electrically connecting batteries to the chargers was poorly designed. Modifications were carried out which included provision of DC circuit-breakers, an electrical proving system, polarity sensing protection and an automatic smoke/fume detection system.

97    On 23 April 1991, a fire occurred in the marine running tunnel north at an electrical transformer installed in a cross-passage. The Control Centre was initially alerted by rises in the carbon monoxide level indicated by the tunnel fixed environmental monitoring stations. Limited evacuation of staff from the tunnels was carried out. Investigation revealed that the most likely cause was a poor connection on the low voltage side of the transformer leading to local overheating. This type of transformer was taken out of use.

98    HSE also pressed for a high standard of fire protection for the 11 kilovolt (kV) construction main supply cable. This is considered in more detail in Chapter 11.

## Static and mobile plant and equipment

99    Several incidents demonstrated the need to assess the potential fire risks for both fixed and mobile plant and equipment before they were taken into use in the underground workings. There were three main problems: firstly, that leaking oil or lubricant could be ignited by the hot plant; secondly, that combustible material used in the plant itself could be ignited; and finally, there was a risk that other flammable material, eg acoustic insulation, could subsequently become involved in the fire.

### Compressors

100    On 1 November 1990, an electrician was affected by smoke inhalation when he attempted to shut off the fans in a compressor enclosure in the UK crossover. The primary cause of the fire was ignition of an oil mist caused by a leak (in the form of a spray) of compressed oil from a flexible hose. The smoke was caused by burning polyurethane foam acoustic lining inside the compressor. The remedial actions taken were:

(a)    to remove foam from other plant;

(b)    to provide a better standard of flexible couplings within the units to reduce the risk of danger;

(c)    to provide remote isolation of this plant.

### Exhaust treatment units (ETUs)

101    There were three incidents in 1991 which were caused by plant provided for the control of exhaust fumes from diesel equipment. These exhaust treatment units were intended to remove oxides of nitrogen and particulates. They were fitted in addition to the catalytic converters in the locomotive silencers which converted carbon monoxide to carbon dioxide. The operating principle of the ETUs was that the exhaust gases leaving the silencer/catalytic converter passed through a flexible pipe to a heat exchanger which cooled the gases to about 90°C. From this the exhaust gases passed to a water spray unit which washed out the particulates, and any acidic compounds were neutralised by an alkaline material in the water spray. Finally the gases were passed through a charcoal bed where oxides of nitrogen were absorbed (see Figure 4).

102    In the first incident, an ETU attached to a 60 kV generator caught fire because a filter had not been installed in the water cooling system. Contaminants blocked the water sprays allowing hot exhaust gases to set the charcoal alight. In the second incident, an ETU attached to a 340 kV generator on a concreting train caught fire in the land running tunnel north. The water spray system was not switched on prior to entry into the tunnel and the hot gases contacted and ignited the charcoal filter. As a result, all three land tunnels were evacuated. Several weeks later, an ETU attached to a diesel locomotive caught fire. The unit had not been switched on prior to tunnel entry and hot gases ignited the charcoal again.

103    Following these incidents, the use of ETUs was suspended and necessary modifications were identified. These included the provision of upgrading of flow detectors for the water supply, thermostatic temperature controls for the charcoal units, a by-pass valve for exhaust gases if a problem occurred within the unit, suitable alarms and a daily inspection routine. Fortunately no one was affected by the three incidents. However these defects might have been revealed had a fire risk assessment of the units been carried out before use.

### Unimog rail and road vehicles

104    On 6 November 1991, a Unimog rail and road diesel vehicle which belonged to the trackwork contractors, Channel Tunnel Trackwork Group, caught fire while shunting on the UK terminal. Flames were seen coming from beneath the cab close to the battery compartment. Attempts to extinguish the fire using hand-held equipment were not successful and Kent Fire Brigade was called to assist. The vehicle cab was completely burned and all interior trim and cabling was destroyed; portions of the two front tyres were burned through to the webbing. Fortunately, this occurred above ground rather than in the tunnel system, although the plant was normally used underground.

**Figure 4**  Exhaust treatment unit schematic diagram

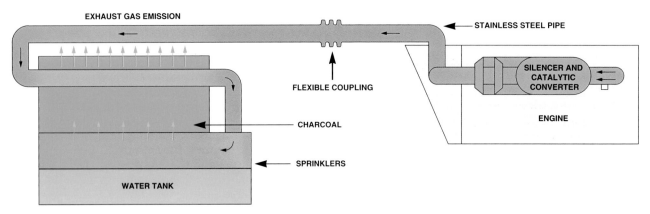

EXHAUST GAS EMISSION

STAINLESS STEEL PIPE

FLEXIBLE COUPLING

CHARCOAL

SPRINKLERS

WATER TANK

SILENCER AND CATALYTIC CONVERTER

ENGINE

DIESEL LOCOMOTIVE

105    All similar vehicles were withdrawn from the tunnel by TLJV until investigations into possible causes were finished. It was concluded that the most likely cause was an electrical fault, or the ignition of hydraulic oil leaking onto the hot exhaust manifold. Remedial measures were implemented which included electrical circuitry checks, provision of covers for exhaust manifolds and relocation of some joints in the hydraulic pipework.

*Conveyors*

106    Substantial conveyor systems were provided for spoil removal. Conveyor systems are well known for making a significant contribution to fire loading as well as providing an ignition source when in use. Spoil removal conveyors were fitted with safety devices such as slipping belt detectors, misalignment detectors, blocked chute probes, drive gearbox oil temperature monitoring and motor thermostats. Also, with one exception, the belting was to NCB 158 standard, the mining standard for conveyor belting. However, there were several smoke and fume incidents at the conveyors, several of which should have been prevented by the safety devices in place. HSE considered that it was principally a failure to ensure proper maintenance so that the safety measures in place were effective. Maintenance of the safety devices for these systems is essential in view of the arduous conditions under which they operate.

**Use of diesel fuel**

107    Use of diesel fuel underground increased significantly as the project progressed. The original intention to use battery/electric locomotives had to be changed because of operating difficulties. Diesel locomotives were introduced on the construction gauge railway and these typically carried a maximum fuel load of about 400 litres of diesel. Because of the logistics of operations, the majority of diesel locomotives had to be refuelled underground and eventually the diesel refuelling stations were located in two parts of the Shakespeare Cliff marshalling area.

108    In 1990 and again in 1992, HSE convened meetings of its experts to consider what effect the use of diesel fuel and the underground refuelling operation had on the fire loading in the project. An additional factor considered at the 1992 meeting was that the locomotives which had recently started to work on the newly installed standard gauge railways in the running tunnels had fuel capacities of up to 4000 litres.

109    A number of control measures had been introduced by TLJV:

(a)    Halon fire suppression systems were fitted to the engines of construction gauge locomotives.

(b)     All combustible materials (foam in driver's seat etc) were removed from locomotives before they were brought into use.

(c)     The diesel refuelling supply was provided with flow sensing and cut-off valves, regulated pumps and monitoring systems.

110     HSE concluded that, because of the control measures put in place by TLJV, the comparative difficulty of igniting diesel fuel and the fact that other fire loads were reduced, diesel fuel did not present a significant increase in fire risk. TLJV had to monitor that the control measures were kept in place and had to be vigilant to ensure that pipework was located away from areas of danger where it could be damaged by passing locomotives and ensure a good standard of housekeeping. From time to time inspectors found that housekeeping in the diesel refuelling areas was not good.

## Smoking

111     TLJV initially resisted HSE pressure to prohibit smoking underground on the basis that it would be an impracticable policy to enforce. However, HSE served an Improvement Notice in December 1987 requiring that a 'no smoking' policy should be implemented in the underground workings. Although throughout the lifetime of the project there were instances where this policy was breached, in the main TLJV were able to prevent smoking underground. Part of the random checks carried out on employees and visitors going underground consisted of searches for smoking materials. Smoking underground was made a dismissible offence. HSE believes that prohibition of smoking underground contributed not only to better control of ignition of flammable materials, but also to better awareness of risk from fire.

## Welding and burning operations

112     The permit-to-burn certificate mentioned in paragraph 92 was a very important method of controlling burning and welding operations to reduce fire risk. In particular, effective permit systems ensure that:

(a)     cylinder sets are restricted to the minimum required (two or three sets underground if possible);

(b)     each set has its own unique identification which is written in the permit and a copy of the permit is available with the equipment;

(c)   permits-to-burn are issued for as short a time as possible, preferably for one shift only, transport permitting, and in any case never for more than one series of shifts;

(d)   all employees and supervisors are encouraged to question the presence of compressed flammable gas equipment not in use, or the validity of any permit for that which is in use.

**Summary of fire safety matters**

●   All work needs to be planned to prevent or minimise the use of flammable gases underground.

●   Electrical equipment for use underground needs to be carefully selected to minimise fire risk.

●   The safety of unattended plant and equipment such as compressors and battery charging equipment is increased with the provision of automatic fire detection systems.

●   Conveyor systems need to be constructed to NCB 158 standard and be provided with monitoring devices to detect overheating etc. Maintenance of conveyors by strict schedule is important.

●   Plant and equipment (mobile and fixed) needs to be assessed before being brought into use so that combustible materials are removed or, if this is not practicable, their use is minimised.

●   Smoking should not be permitted underground and all smoking materials should be left at the surface.

●   Adequate safety devices are needed for diesel refuelling and good standards of cleanliness should be maintained.

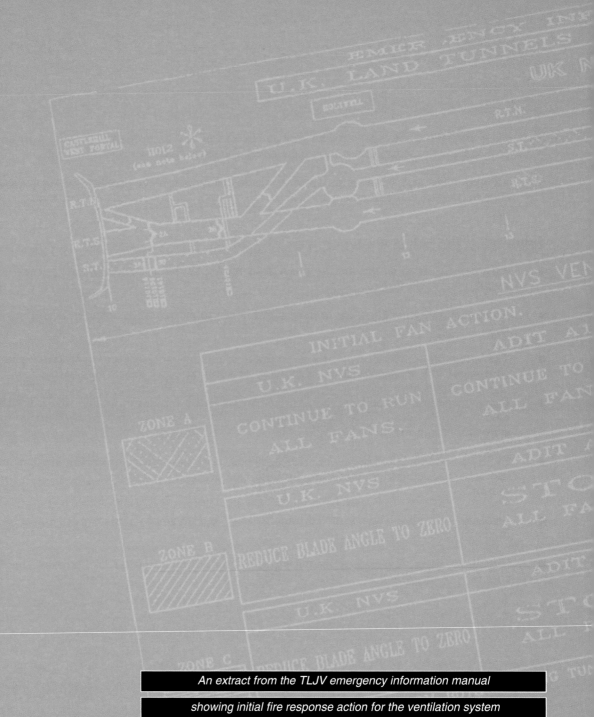

An extract from the TLJV emergency information manual

*showing initial fire response action for the ventilation system*

# CHAPTER SIX

## Emergency procedures

49

## Introduction

113 As the project developed, elements of the work became increasingly complex. In the UK, during the tunnelling phase, six tunnels were being driven at approximately the same time and the UK marine crossover and two major undersea pumping stations were being constructed in the marine tunnels. In addition, work on cross-passages and piston relief ducts continued. In some ways the period following the final marine tunnel breakthroughs in mid-1991 saw the most diverse range of activities as the major tasks of fitting out and commissioning the system progressed. HSE and TLJV were concerned to ensure that procedures were in place to address foreseeable emergencies. These procedures were developed and continually updated to keep pace with the ever changing conditions underground. They were designed to deal with all risks, with the three major concerns perceived to be fire, flooding and collision/derailment of trains. However, the most significant risk remained that of the outbreak of fire, particularly in a blind heading, and many of the detailed emergency procedures reflected this preoccupation.

## Early detection and alerting

114 There were three ways of raising the alarm in the event of a fire:

(a) visual detection and reporting using one of the communications systems described in paragraph 135;

(b) automatic local detection, which was linked with fire suppression at specific plant such as on the TBMs, the locomotives and the compressors;

(c) continuous tunnel environmental monitoring giving direct read-out to the Control Centre (described in paragraph 117).

115 All employees received training in ways to raise the alarm. There were four alternative methods of communication between the underground workings and the Control Centre at Shakespeare Cliff which managed emergencies. It was essential that everyone underground knew what these methods were.

116 Certain areas of the TBMs, together with some other equipment such as unattended compressors, were provided with automatic fire detection and alarm equipment (which was described in Chapters 4 and 5). This was not always provided spontaneously by TLJV and was often brought about by the action of HSE or as a result of a fire or smoke incident. As the project developed, so did the concept that automatic detection should be provided for plant which could present a fire risk when left unattended.

117    A fixed environmental monitoring system was initially trialled early in the project and later extended to the whole of the tunnel complex. It consisted of stations in the main tunnels and cross-passages where groups of detectors which gave continuous direct read-out to the Control Centre were located. Functions monitored included oxygen and carbon monoxide levels, temperature and the concentration of flammable gases. At strategic locations, carbon dioxide, nitrogen dioxide and nitrogen oxide were also measured. This facility became an important tool in providing early warning of a developing incident. Although there were difficulties from time to time in maintaining the sensors and ensuring their optimum location, they played an increasing role in the effective management of an emergency such as the outbreak of fire.

**Arrangements for fire fighting**

118    Although the priority in emergencies in tunnels is to escape, it is important to make provision for fire fighting, both to deal with small fires to prevent them growing and to contain larger fires which might otherwise prevent people from escaping.

119    Methods of fire fighting were as follows:

(a)    A fully-charged fire main was located in each tunnel with hose reels at appropriate locations such as cross-passages. This equipment was primarily intended for use by the fire brigade.

(b)    Dry powder fire extinguishers were provided at each cross-passage and at other locations, eg beside the diesel refuelling points, on TBMs and at every location where groups of people were working. The provision of portable extinguishers was incorporated into the permit-to-burn for cutting and welding operations.

(c)    The TBMs were fitted with foam suppression systems and water spray barriers (as described in Chapter 4). This ensured that a major fire could be controlled long enough to allow escape procedures. Without this provision of fire-fighting equipment on TBMs, heat and pollutants might quickly overcome those trying to escape.

(d)    Certain other mobile plant (eg diesel locomotives) was provided with fire suppression systems.

**Escape**

120    From the start of the project, HSE was concerned to ensure that the contractors addressed the issue of means of escape to a safer location for all phases of the work. Initially, attention was focused on emergency escape from TBMs working in blind headings. As the project developed, there were numerous other work locations, such as the crossover cavern, from which the means of escape had to be pre-planned. Changes in the tunnel layout as work progressed meant that the means of escape had to be reviewed periodically for the different phases of the project as follows:

(a)    Escape out of the blind heading as first the marine service tunnel and, later, the land service tunnel was being driven in advance of the two running tunnels.

(b)    Then, as the marine running tunnels progressed to follow behind the marine service tunnel, physical separation of the tunnels was carried out to provide at least one smoke-free escape tunnel.

(c)    Finally, after breakthrough of the UK and French marine tunnels, an escape tunnel was kept free of smoke by using a balanced ventilation system.

121    All employees were provided with a self-rescuer which gives some protection against increased levels of carbon monoxide resulting from fire. However it could not compensate for oxygen deficiency. Also, protected trains were located permanently at the rear of the TBMs. These trains were fitted with compressed air systems to which face masks could be attached.

122    In 1990, before breakthrough of the marine service tunnel, emergency cross-passages were opened between the three tunnels as they were extended. These cross-passages were fitted with substantial doors to separate the tunnels.

123    From the beginning of the project, emergency lighting had been provided in the tunnels which operated automatically in the event of a power failure. However, there were several occasions on which this failed, leading to partial blackouts, and this indicated a need to ensure that emergency lighting was installed correctly as construction progressed.

124    The progressive breakthrough of the UK and French marine tunnels and the start of fixed equipment installations had a number of important consequences:

(a)    The whole of the underground workings were accessible from both France and the UK. This allowed people to escape in two directions.

(b)    With the start of the fixed equipment phase, work had to be carried out in numerous cross-passages and piston relief ducts simultaneously so that it was no longer practicable to rely on the doors in the cross-passages to prevent smoke passing between the tunnels.

(c)    The ventilation system was changed from being provided in ducts to the TBMs to full-face tunnel ventilation driven by mid-point fan stations.

(d)    TLJV revised their emergency response based on controlling the new ventilation system by switching individual banks of fans on or off to maintain at least one tunnel free of smoke in the event of fire.

125    Breakthrough of the marine running tunnels in the early summer of 1991, followed by the construction of the mid-point fan stations, meant that by the late summer of 1991, ventilation could be provided through the whole tunnel system. This ventilation system drew air from the portal at the UK terminal through a fan station inside the tunnel at Holywell, to Shakespeare Cliff, where much escaped up the shaft and adit A2. The remaining air from the portal, with additional air supplied through adit A1, was drawn into all three UK marine tunnels by the mid-point fans to pass to France where it exhausted through the Sangatte shaft and the French terminal portal.

126    TLJV developed a system to manage the ventilation which enabled one tunnel to remain unaffected by smoke in the event of a fire, thus producing a safe haven to facilitate escape. The contractors claimed that by so doing, physical separation of the tunnels was no longer required. The system was managed by a ventilation engineer in the Control Room (engineers shared a 24-hour shift duty) who ensured that a balanced airflow was maintained in each of the tunnels in such a way that minimal air passed from one tunnel to the next. TLJV developed a series of annotated diagrams, known as fire response diagrams, showing the balanced ventilation system and the actions necessary in emergencies.

127    HSE required that the contractors prove, by computer modelling, that the balanced ventilation system could achieve the objective of a smoke-free tunnel. Earlier, HSE had commissioned a consultancy, Cambridge Environmental Research Consultants (CERC), to carry out computer modelling work for HSE's risk assessment of the use of mineral oils on TBMs. TLJV now agreed to employ CERC to model the ventilation system and in 1991 and 1992 the consultants carried out this work. The computer model and its validation are described in Appendix 2.

128    Several real incidents also demonstrated that the balanced ventilation system was effective. In one particular incident in June 1992, a diesel-powered generator on a concreting

train became defective when the main filter for the generator was blocked by concrete dust. There was a rise in the level of carbon monoxide in the running tunnel in which the equipment was located. TLJV evacuated personnel from that tunnel to the safe marine running tunnel and called out the emergency services. In fact, there were higher than expected carbon monoxide levels in the marine service tunnel but the system was balanced to provide a haven in the adjacent running tunnel. While this aspect of balanced ventilation was new to the Channel Tunnel, it may have application for other multiple-bore tunnels in future.

**Rescue and control of emergencies**

129    Even with escape procedures in place, it was foreseeable that people could be left behind in emergencies. There were a number of problems:

(a)    Information communicated to the Control Centre from underground had to be verified before deployment of the TLJV rescue team and the emergency services.

(b)    In managing underground transport in an emergency, priority had to be given to those trains which were being used for escape; at the same time, trains had to be provided and made ready for rescue.

(c)    In the earlier stages of the project, while TBMs were still working in blind headings, there were serious questions about how it would be possible for the emergency services to carry out deep tunnel rescue through extended lengths of smoke and pollutants.

130    TLJV set up an emergency control room in the Control Centre in which all the emergency services had access to telephone and other communication systems as well as to Control Centre information, such as environmental conditions in the tunnels. The main lesson learned during emergency exercises was that lines of communication had to be clear to ensure effective rescue.

131    The Control Centre also had direct management of the transport system in an emergency and TLJV had arrangements to identify the whereabouts of trains and rolling stock (and later, wheeled vehicles which travelled in the service tunnel on the final concrete floor).

132    The earlier problem of deploying the emergency services and TLJV's rescue teams in smoke-filled tunnels was alleviated by the provision of two protected rescue trains to enable the rescue teams to penetrate into the tunnel system. These trains enabled the emergency

teams to go underground to a point where they could put on their long-duration breathing apparatus and leave the vehicle.

133    The essential feature of the management of emergencies was that those handling the emergency had defined tasks and only one person was in overall control. This person, the main controller, was a nominated senior site manager who was trained in dealing with emergencies. In any emergency, the main controller and the emergency services worked together in the Control Room so that decisions were taken based on the best information available. After breakthrough of the marine service tunnel, TLJV, the emergency services and HSE also worked to an agreed written binational emergency plan which had been developed by the Safety Authority's Rescue and Public Safety Working Group. The essence of the plan was to ensure effective decision-making, co-ordination and communication in the event of an emergency.

134    Effective management of an emergency depended on:

(a)    the Control and Communications Centre which was staffed by trained and experienced personnel and which had facilities to accommodate emergency services;

(b)    effective communication links between the Control Centre and the scene of the incident.

135    There were four methods of communication:

(a)    channelled VHF radio communications with a dedicated emergency channel. Most employees out of normal reach of communication systems carried VHF radios;

(b)    a standard telephone communication system which was provided at cross-passages;

(c)    the tunnel public address (PA) system. This was tested on numerous occasions and inspectors witnessed effective information provided by it. All employees were issued with an instruction card for emergencies which described the signals which would be transmitted across the PA system to indicate emergencies;

(d)    a fire survivable emergency telephone system which was provided at strategic points, eg on the TBMs and at the UK crossover.

136    The communication methods were developed and refined as the project continued. The essential feature was that there were alternative means of communicating in the event of the failure or destruction of any one system.

**Accounting for personnel**

137　A system of accounting for personnel is of paramount importance in any tunnel operation. In overall terms the system employed was as follows:

(a)　A controlled secure zone for entry into the tunnels. Controlled turnstiles were located in this zone; on passing through one, the employee gave up his turnstile pass for a self-rescuer, retrieving the turnstile pass when he returned from the underground workings.

(b)　In addition to the self-rescuer, two metal tallies were given in exchange for the pass. Because of the complexity of the underground workings, tally boards were eventually located at the entrances to all the tunnels. One of the tallies was then placed on the board and the other was kept by the employee. Although this required some self-discipline, the system generally worked. In tunnelling operations where there is only one point of entry and egress, it is relatively simple to put the tally board there under the control of an employee who will take tallies from those going underground. Another advantage of this system is that it is a very efficient way of counting and then identifying those tallies which remain on the board during emergencies.

(c)　Eventually the tunnel system became so complex that a computer entry card system was used. This provided a printout of all people entering and the time of their entry and return.

(d)　Certain activities, eg trains being used as work stations, were reported into the Control Centre and were monitored so that the Centre was always aware of the location of trains.

(e)　Permits-to-work were used and eventually so were work authorisation documents which identified the areas where employees were working.

138　Emergency exercises were carried out on several occasions. These were vital in highlighting deficiencies and enabling changes to be made following discussion between TLJV and the emergency services. For example, the crucial role of communications and the consequent need for clear procedures was emphasised in both full-scale mobilising exercises and in table-top simulations. Problems of access to the underground workings and access to the site led to changes in procedures for emergencies.

139    There were also several large-scale emergency exercises, one of which, 'Elan' held in May 1991, was binational. HSE inspectors were involved as players as well as observers. A substantial amount of effort was put into the exercises by way of resources and planning which was necessary to ensure that emergency procedures could address any real-life emergency.

**Summary of health and safety issues in emergency procedures**

● It is vital that emergency procedures are drawn up in conjunction with the emergency services, and emergency exercises which involve all parties are crucial to ensure that procedures are valid.

● Emergencies should be managed by one appointed and named manager and there should be enough managers appointed to ensure that a controller is on site at all times while work continues.

● A system of accounting for personnel is essential, using at least a double tally system, its equivalent or better, through a controlled access zone.

● Communication systems have to be sufficient to allow immediate priority communication and there always needs to be at least one alternative system.

● Escape has priority during emergencies. Equipment for escape and rescue should be maintained; procedures should be kept up to date.

*Miners placing the invert (bottom) concrete lining*

*segment in the build area of a tunnel boring machine*

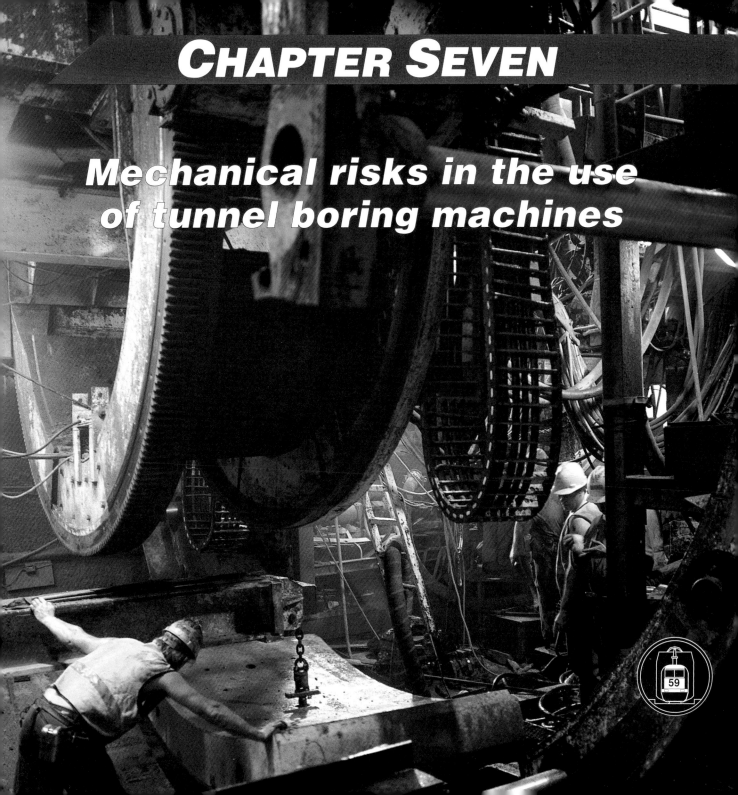

# CHAPTER SEVEN

## Mechanical risks in the use of tunnel boring machines

## Description of the TBMs

140    Six TBMs were used to drive the UK tunnels. They were designed and constructed as three pairs:

(a)    the land and marine service tunnel TBMs manufactured by James Howden Ltd;

(b)    the land running tunnel north and south TBMs also manufactured by James Howden Ltd;

(c)    the marine running tunnel north and south TBMs manufactured by Robbins-Markham Joint Venture.

141    The fundamental design of all three pairs was similar, but there were also important differences between them, eg in the design of the segment erection mechanisms.

142    Each TBM (see Figure 5) consisted of a revolving cutting head [1] equipped with hydraulic grippers and rams which enabled the cutting head to move forward in steps of 1.5 m. This in turn exposed an equivalent section of cut chalk marl behind the cutting head [2] into which the 1.5 m ring of concrete support segments was built. (In certain areas, cast iron segments were used due to ground conditions or to allow removal of some segments for further hand tunnelling.)

143    In this 'build area', the ring was placed in position by miners using different forms of segment erector. On the service tunnel TBMs and initially also on the marine running tunnel TBMs, the lower segments were placed in position using overhead travelling cranes [3], and the upper segments by erectors which rotated through the upper circumference of the tunnel [4]. On the land running tunnel TBMs, and, after modifications were carried out, on the marine running tunnel TBMs, all the segments were placed in position by an erector which covered the full 360° of the tunnel's circumference. A number of other important operations took place in the build area, such as the injection of grout behind the rings and the fixing of the rail track on which the trailers were pulled making up the rear part of the TBM.

144    A conveyor system [5] took the excavated material ('muck') from the cutting head back along the length of the TBM to where it was deposited into rail wagons. Conveyors and lifting equipment were also provided within the TBM to remove the segments and other materials and equipment from the incoming trains and transport them forward to the build area or their place of use. The trailers also held a range of other facilities such as grouting and ventilation equipment, hydraulic and electrical power packs, workshops and mess rooms. The total length of the TBMs was between 200 and 250 m.

**Figure 5**  Cross-section of TBM cutting and front areas

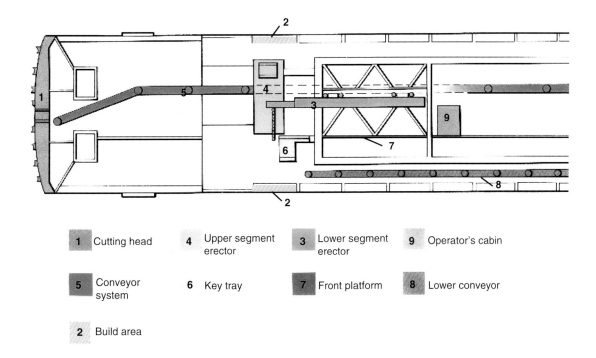

| | | | | | | |
|---|---|---|---|---|---|---|
| **1** | Cutting head | **4** | Upper segment erector | **3** | Lower segment erector | **9** Operator's cabin |
| **5** | Conveyor system | **6** | Key tray | **7** | Front platform | **8** Lower conveyor |
| **2** | Build area | | | | | |

### Mechanical safety

145    TBMs are in practical terms an assembly of a number of separate machines and this is important when considering mechanical safety. The machines handle large and heavy articles in circumstances which can create trapping points:

(a)    between moving parts of the machinery;

(b)    between the moving machinery and the segments;

(c)    between the machinery and the tunnel or fixed parts of the TBM.

146    The available space on the TBMs is filled with equipment and supplies, and the working areas, even on the larger machines, can be confined and difficult. Mechanical hazards on the TBMs were associated principally with four types of equipment: segment erectors, cranes, conveyors and construction plant such as grout mixers.

### Design of TBMs

147    The importance of designing for safety was emphasised throughout the project, both positively, by those aspects of the TBM safeguarding which proved their worth, and negatively, by those problems which might have been resolved during the design stage, but were not. Effective design was important not only in relation to mechanical hazards on the TBMs, but for all aspects of health and safety. Unfortunately, a number of important design criteria were established on the basis of the likely low water ingress levels in the tunnel; the marine drive TBMs then had to be substantially modified on site when conditions in the early stages of the drives turned out to be much wetter than anticipated. This underlines the importance of site investigation both for the design and operation of TBMs.

### Modifications to the marine running tunnel TBMs

148    Running tunnel rings were made up from nine segments. Originally, the segments were put into position in three stages (see Figure 5):

(a)    The lower three segments were placed in position by one of the two lower segment erectors [3]. These were cranes which were designed so that their beams (measuring over 5 m) moved across the whole width of the tunnel and extended and retracted along the length of the tunnel. During the erection of the TBMs, sheet metal guards were fitted to the underside of the lower segment erectors to prevent access to the drive mechanism.

(b)    The five upper segments were moved forward at high level by a transfer device which placed the segments where they could be picked up by the upper segment erector and located in position.

(c)    The key segment (which locked the other eight segments in position) then had to be lifted by the lower segment erector onto a small steel frame known as the key tray [6]. This tray moved forward to where the key segment could be lifted by the upper segment erector and placed in position to complete the ring.

149    The TBMs began work in the first half of 1989, but progress during the summer of that year was slow as they attempted to drive through the very wet ground which extended from near the start of the marine drive to a point about 4 km out from Shakespeare Cliff. TLJV and Robbins-Markham, the manufacturer of the two marine running tunnel TBMs, decided in September 1989 that the TBMs should be modified to ensure that build accuracy was maintained, and that the upper segments in the ring could be grouted as soon as possible after each ring was completed. The upper segment transfer arrangement was removed and replaced by a high-level grouting platform. In consequence, the upper segments then had to be brought to the build area using the low-level cranes and conveyors. It was decided to enlarge the key tray so that it could transfer all the upper segments to a position where they could be picked up by the upper erector. After enlargement, this tray was referred to as the 'segment tray'. These changes had a number of implications for safety on the TBMs.

150    Shortly after the completion of these modifications, a fatal accident occurred in the build area of the TBM in the marine running tunnel south involving Mr Gary Woodward, a miner on the TBM. Mr Woodward was installing a length of rail track used to support the TBM trailers when the segment tray retracted without warning, trapping him between the tray and the main gantry of the TBM.

151    Investigation of the accident revealed that the enlargement of the key tray to enable it to hold all the upper segments had created a trap in an area where miners had to work when installing the TBM rails. In addition, it was discovered that the guards on the underside of the lower segment erector fouled the steelwork at the side of the TBM gantry and had cut through the control cable for the lower segment tray, causing a short-circuit which caused the segment tray to retract, trapping the miner. The control circuit was not referenced to earth; if it had been, the damage to the cable would not have caused the tray to move.

152    TLJV stopped both marine running tunnel TBMs immediately after the accident and agreed to take two immediate steps to prevent a recurrence. These were:

(a)    to provide a physical stop to ensure that the segment trays could not retract closer than 500 mm to fixed steelwork;

(b)    to check the integrity of the electrical control circuits associated with the segment trays and to ensure that one side of the control circuit was earthed. In the event, TLJV decided to remove the electrical control circuit from the segment tray and replace it with a direct hydraulic circuit which failed to safety.

153    Other problems emerged during the investigation, such as the temporary maintenance of electric cabling, and differences in the way the modifications had taken place on the two machines; longer term action was required, relating both to technical issues and to the management of safety. HSE prosecuted both TLJV and Robbins-Markham following this fatal accident.

**Maintenance of TBMs**

154    TLJV had a systematic approach to maintenance, with regular, planned shutdowns allowed for in the production schedules to carry out essential work. However, much TBM maintenance often takes place while production continues, and the problems that this creates are aggravated by the cramped conditions and the working positions which often cannot be seen by others on the machine. These aspects need to be recognised by designers and users of machines and those who draw up maintenance schedules; they also emphasise the importance of formal systems of work for maintenance operations, including isolation and locking-off procedures.

155    The investigation of a fatal accident on the land service tunnel TBM in February 1989 revealed the absence of safe maintenance procedures. An electrician, Mr David Symes, and other members of the maintenance gang with whom he worked, had been repairing part of the conveyor system during the night shift and had worked with their heads and upper bodies between fixed parts of the TBM and above the level of the travelling beam of the segment handling cranes. The cranes had not been isolated and locked off during this work and the lives of the workers involved were put at considerable risk; fortunately, while the main part of the work was going on no cranes had been used. Subsequently Mr Symes returned to the area where he and the gang had been working, but this time the cranes were in use and he was trapped between a crane and the TBM framework. TLJV were prosecuted by HSE for failing to

ensure safety during the earlier maintenance operation. Lack of evidence as to Mr Symes' later actions meant that the details of the fatal accident were not part of the prosecution.

156    Immediately after the accident, new procedures were instituted which required TLJV to identify areas where trapping could occur and the institution of a safe system of work (including isolation and physical locking-off of the power supply) when work had to be carried out in those areas.

157    Electrical isolators and other power sources which control dangerous moving parts of TBMs require lock-off devices. There are numerous proprietary systems which allow a number of fitters, electricians and others doing maintenance to lock-off an isolator by a single padlock which cannot be re-energised until all have used their separate keys to release the padlock. Locking-off should be seen as part of a permit-to-work system which ensures that no other dangerous actions can take place while plant is being maintained.

## Work locations on TBMs

158    One of the lessons to emerge most clearly from the Channel Tunnel experience is that it is reasonably foreseeable that operatives will have to work in virtually any location on a TBM during production, and failure to take account of this can lead to accidents. This was tragically demonstrated on 7 May 1990 in the lower erector area of the running tunnel north TBM when Mr William Cartman, a grouter, was killed.

159    Grout was injected between completed sections of the tunnel lining and the rock face to limit water ingress. For the greater part of the boring of the marine running tunnels up to the period shortly before the accident, ground conditions had been poor and there had been substantial ingress. An accelerator had been added to the grout to cause it to set quickly and thus reduce water flows. However, ground conditions improved, and five days before the accident a joint TLJV and Eurotunnel decision was made to stop using accelerator. Another effect of the use of accelerator was that the grout would normally travel only a short distance behind the segments before setting; the effect of not using the accelerator was that it travelled further behind the completed rings. Grout would from time to time – more frequently with non-accelerated grout – leak through the joints between the segments, and it was common practice for grouters to push pieces of material into the leaking joints to help seal them.

160    It appears that Mr Cartman went to the platform (see [7] on Figure 5) where the two lower segment erectors were located, in an attempt to seal a leak of grout at a joint between two completed tunnel rings. The operator of the lower erector could not see the grouter and

moved the erector to one side; as he did so, Mr Cartman was trapped and crushed between the erector beam and the outer framework of the TBM. The written procedure for erector operators did not take account of the fact that parts of the erector platform were not visible from the operator's normal position. After the accident, HSE issued a Prohibition Notice which stopped both marine running tunnel TBMs until the lower segment erector area had been made safe. HSE also prosecuted TLJV.

161     At the time of the accident, TLJV and Robbins-Markham were planning further major modifications to the TBMs and their response to the Prohibition Notice was in two phases. On one machine, a temporary interlocked barrier was installed with direct supervision to prevent access through, and work in, the lower erector area unless the erectors were not working. The other machine remained shut down until the planned modification programme could be brought forward. This programme consisted of converting the upper segment erector to a 360° erector and changing the complex lower conveyor arrangement [8] so that it delivered all segments into position where they could be picked up directly by the modified upper erector. The segment tray which had caused the fatal accident to Gary Woodward (see paragraph 150) became redundant and was removed as a part of the modifications. The lower erectors might have been retained under the original programme, but following the accident they too were removed. As a result of these changes, the mechanical safety risks at the front end of both machines were substantially reduced, and the production efficiency substantially increased.

## Production changes

162     Changes in production methods occur in tunnelling on a regular basis, particularly as ground conditions change. It is necessary to assess whether such changes will have an effect upon health and safety, even though at first sight there may be no obvious direct impact. When the key tray of the TBM in the marine running tunnel south was enlarged, TLJV and Robbins-Markham should have identified the risk to the miner who had to enter that area to bolt up the rails.

163     The removal of the accelerator from the grout in the running tunnel north TBM was an example of the less direct effect of production changes on health and safety. Even in that case, it was reasonably foreseeable that there might be grout leaks in relatively remote positions which grouters would have to attend to and an assessment should have been made of how such work could safely take place.

164     The logic of this approach – looking at each of the elements in turn when a procedure is altered – is now central to the legal requirements for risk assessment and a number of incidents

occurred in the tunnel which emphasised the importance of assessing risks arising out of production changes.

## Summary of reduction of mechanical risk at TBMs

- Designers and manufacturers of TBMs need to assess in full all mechanical hazards and should not introduce unnecessary hazard into areas which are potential normal places of work.

- All subsequent on-site modifications to TBMs need to be properly evaluated and the resultant mechanical hazards need to be fully addressed.

- A permit-to-work system which ensures that power sources are isolated and locked off is vital to maintenance safety.

- Work locations in TBMs have to be defined and any area where unavoidable mechanical hazard exists should be effectively controlled.

- Time should be allowed (eg by use of the permit-to-work system) to deal with problems arising from modifications, maintenance and production difficulties.

- All production changes need to be assessed for their effect on health and safety.

Miners using power tools during excavation

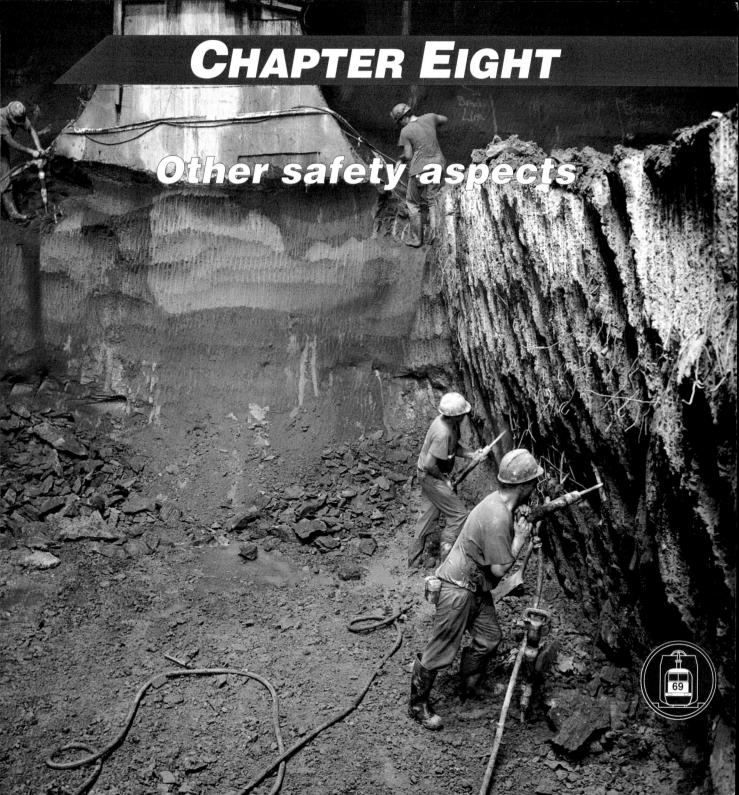

# CHAPTER EIGHT

## Other safety aspects

69

## Introduction

165    This chapter examines four topics which had to be considered in detail or caused concern during the project. These are:

(a)    the provision of safe access within TBMs and through the tunnels;

(b)    the tunnelling technique known as New Austrian Tunnelling Method (NATM) which is based on excavation by machinery followed by a system of supporting the excavated face;

(c)    protection measures taken against flooding;

(d)    construction of the sea wall at Shakespeare Cliff.

## Provision of safe access within TBMs and through the tunnels

### Service tunnel TBMs

166    Access to the service tunnel TBMs was difficult because:

(a)    the rear parts of the service tunnel TBMs were essentially a series of trailers through which there was an access way about 600 mm wide. Because of the variety of activities which took place along the length of the trailers, materials and plant constantly encroached onto this access way;

(b)    it was particularly difficult to keep the access corridor free on the marine service tunnel TBM. Part of the problem was that the very wet ground which was encountered in the first 4 km led to much greater use of grout and sealing materials than had originally been envisaged. It was only when the wetter ground was left behind and the transfer of materials in and out of the TBM was better controlled that it became easier to maintain a clear passageway. Tunnelling projects should plan for the possibility of increased use of materials due, for example, to poor ground conditions and allow for appropriate storage space on the TBMs;

(c)    along the length of the TBM trailers, the side of the passageway next to the railway track was well fenced. However, between the trailers there were gaps and a number of accidents occurred in the early stages when personnel stepped or stumbled down onto the track as trains were passing. It was necessary to provide additional guard-rails to prevent falling through these gaps between trailers;

(d)    no specific provision was designed into the TBMs for safe access from the trailers to the build area at the front of the machine. This last stage was filled with temporary boarding or walkways which were often damaged and became slippery or unstable. It is essential that safe and durable walkways are provided to all areas to which anyone may need access. This should be planned into the design of TBMs.

### Marine running tunnel TBMs

167    When the first marine running tunnel TBM was erected, it was anticipated that the restricted and difficult access which had been a feature in the marine service tunnel TBM would be eliminated. To an extent, this proved to be the case as the second TBM had four walkways, two on each side at the upper and lower level, running virtually the full length of the TBM. However, problems occurred early on with the communication ladders between the upper and lower walkways and in particular with the access trap doors in the upper walkways. These were heavy and difficult to lift from below, and when raised, left an opening in the walkway through which people could fall. TLJV concluded that it was not possible to ensure that they would be kept closed when not in use. The number of openings was reduced and barriers were fixed on either side of the openings that remained.

168    The main access difficulties at these TBMs occurred in the parts of the TBM immediately behind the build area (where the segments were erected). It was necessary to pass from the back platform of this area, where segments were unloaded from the railway wagons, past the TBM control cabin and through the front lower erector gantry, the latter being about 2.5 m above the invert of the tunnel. The problems were:

(a)    the unprotected edges at the rear of the segment unloading area and at the opening in the decking of the platform where segments had to be lowered onto the lower segment conveyor. There was also a risk of falling from the edge of the build area itself;

(b)    the traps created by the materials handling equipment in conjunction with fixed parts of the structure, in particular, the cranes at the unloading area and the lower segment erectors in the gantry area. The problem of mechanical risk in the latter area was considered in detail in Chapter 7;

71

(c)     the arrangements for removing damaged segments or other materials from the build area. On the machines as supplied this facility consisted of a large array of up-turned castors on the right-hand side of the front gantry deck. The castors created a foreseeable and significant tripping hazard which could result in injury by falling onto the castors, falling against the framework of the machine or falling from the edge of the gantry into the build area;

(d)     the ladders which gave access from the front erector gantry down into the invert of the build area. These ladders were frequently struck by swaying segments and other heavy equipment and were often damaged.

169     HSE served an Improvement Notice on TLJV in September 1989 regarding the above access problems. TLJV complied with the Notice by taking the following action:

(a)     providing fencing and other protection at the segment unloading area to prevent falls from the edge and covering the opening through which segments were lowered onto the conveyor;

(b)     removing the castors from the lower erector crane gantry;

(c)     fitting an extended metal stop between the two segment erector cranes;

(d)     replacing the ladders, allowing access into the invert of the build area with strengthened ones;

(e)     instituting a control system for access through the lower erector crane gantry, although this system was not maintained and became ineffective (see Chapter 7).

### Land running tunnel TBMs

170     On the land running tunnel TBMs, the upper working area at the rear of each TBM was not provided with effective edge protection. Materials had to be transferred to and from the upper working platform and it was difficult to maintain fixed handrails in position. Eventually a system involving the use of both fixed and removable handrails was adopted.

171     On the same TBMs, cement and grout bags had to be lifted from the railway wagon to the grouting area on the upper platform. An opening was provided in the upper platform which was not protected. This problem was resolved by taking the area out of use and covering the

opening, and lifting the material to the upper platform using equipment installed on another part of the TBM.

### Common TBM access problems

172    On both land and marine running tunnel TBMs, equipment obstructed access from the invert of the tunnel up onto the TBM walkway. Although there were plans to direct cables and pipework into the TBM via a different route, these arrangements did not prove to be adequate and the services were often directed into the TBM in the area of the rear access way.

173    Other access problems which occurred on the TBMs included access at high level in the build area for grouting and alignment purposes; access through the cutting head of the TBM for maintenance purposes; and access in front of the cutting head to maintain the cutters and to carry out geological analysis. TLJV and HSE addressed these problems throughout the project. The solutions often depended on appropriate careful design of access taking into account hazards which could be avoided entirely or protected against.

### General access through the tunnels

174    The use of transport within the tunnels and its effect on the safety of those walking or working in tunnels are described in Chapter 10. Paragraphs 175 and 176 examine the underfoot conditions when walking in tunnels.

175    The invert of the service tunnel had a flat floor, formed by slabs resting on the lower segments, and this made walking relatively easy. However, the running tunnels had no invert slab and the rails were laid upon concrete blocks which lifted the track some 600 mm above the lowest point of the tunnel. This system made the tunnel extremely difficult to walk through other than by stepping from block to block. During the early stages, TLJV placed boards across the blocks, but this was not satisfactory, and the inverts of the running tunnels were later infilled to provide a level surface and to make it easier to deal with transport problems.

176    Also, on either side of the running tunnels, a ledge was cast into the segments which ran the entire length of the tunnel; this later was built on to form the walkway to be used for emergency evacuation when the tunnel became operational. This ledge or 'haunch' was used by the workforce for walking in the tunnel and also as the effective refuge when trains passed. Experiments were made during the early part of the project to provide a guard-rail on the outside of the haunch, but because it was difficult to maintain and it prevented easy access on and off the haunch, it was not used. With hindsight it would have been more satisfactory to provide a hand-holding rail along the tunnel wall adjacent to the haunch walkway.

## The New Austrian Tunnelling Method

177    The New Austrian Tunnelling Method (NATM) was used to design and construct the new adit (A2) from the lower Shakespeare Cliff area to the tunnel workings, the three tunnels under Castle Hill, the TBM build chambers and marshalling areas under Shakespeare Cliff and the UK marine crossover chamber which was located 7 km out under the sea from Shakespeare Cliff.

178    In the Channel Tunnel, NATM was carried out as follows:

(a)    An incremental excavation, usually between about 1 m and 3 m, was authorised after the technical consideration, at least once a day, of a number of factors, including the local ground conditions and results from ground measurement and monitoring devices.

(b)    Immediately after the ground had been exposed, the excavated faces were sprayed with a thin (50 mm) layer of concrete (shotcrete) which provided short-term stability.

(c)    Lattice steel girders and reinforcing steel mesh were then positioned according to the design requirements and secured to this first layer of shotcrete. A further second layer of shotcrete was then applied to complete the primary NATM lining.

(d)    If the ground at the crown of the cross-section was considered weak, then spiles were driven to support the top of the next part of the excavation prior to removing further material.

(e)    Finally, bolts were secured into drilled holes at specified distances to provide ground reinforcement. The temporary NATM lining was designed to take the anticipated load during construction. It was later incorporated into the permanent works with the pouring of an *in situ* concrete lining using movable shutters.

179    The main problems associated with NATM at the Channel Tunnel site concerned access and transport risks and certain health matters (see Chapter 9). It was anticipated that there would be some risk of collapse of unsupported faces during excavation, but serious falls of material did not occur. However, some projects which have used this technique, or a variation of it, have experienced problems. Following a tunnel collapse at Heathrow Airport in late 1994, a detailed HSE investigation is in progress at the time of writing and it is important to consider its findings in future projects.

180    To construct the large chambers (the TBM build chambers and the UK crossover), incremental excavation using roadheaders (which have revolving cutting heads mounted at the end of a jib) was undertaken on different levels from the crown of the tunnel downwards. This technique created multiple levels of work until the whole cross-section of the excavation was complete. There were few planned access walkways and reliance was often placed on scrambling along the sides of NATM excavations or along narrow ledges above voids or other work areas. Large-scale NATM operations need to be provided with planned access arrangements designed to avoid the risk of people falling.

181    Another problem during NATM was created by the use of large slewing excavators and roadheaders:

(a)    When using roadheaders in the tunnel invert, personnel sometimes passed on the narrow, excavated, uneven ledges above the roadheaders. This created the serious risk of falling into the path of the cutting head. Action was taken to prevent access above these machines while they were in use.

(b)    Machinery capable of slewing, such as excavators, had to work in areas where there was not sufficient clearance to pass safely between machinery and either fixed plant or the side of the tunnel. An accident occurred during the development of the bottom end of adit A2 when an employee was trapped between the moving excavator and the tunnel wall. The excavator being used on that occasion was too large for the space in which it was working and it was replaced by a smaller machine. In addition to the size of machines, exclusion barriers and notices are required for such work.

**Flooding**

182    The alignment of the Channel Tunnel runs almost entirely along a section of chalk marl, a mixture of chalk and clay, which has a minimum thickness of 25 m beneath the Channel. The lowest point in the tunnel is about 15 km offshore from Shakespeare Cliff where the chalk marl lies almost 75 m below the sea bed. From a tunnelling point of view, chalk marl is easier to excavate and support than the chalk which lies above it and the Gault Clay which lies below it.

183    Over the years, more than 100 deep boreholes were drilled along the likely line of a Channel tunnel and substantial marine geophysical surveys were carried out. A major flow of water into the undersea workings, either through a fissure in the rock or through an ungrouted borehole in the bed of the Channel, was always regarded as a risk, although a remote one. It was believed that the locations of all the boreholes were logged and that most had been

properly grouted. However, it was recognised that some might not have been and the TBMs were designed to cope with striking an ungrouted borehole.

184    Probe drilling was carried out as the marine service tunnel TBM progressed along the line of the tunnels. This consisted of drilling 100 m ahead through the face of the TBM so that it was always operating in probed ground. Lateral probe drilling also took place.

185    In spite of the range of survey and testing work, TLJV recognised that the marine TBMs might suffer an uncontrolled flooding. This was dealt with in two ways:

(a)    To prevent a backflow of water along the side of the machine to the unsupported ground in front of the build area, the head of each marine drive TBM was equipped with a circumferential seal and an emergency bulkhead door which was designed to seal off the conveyor opening in the cutter head.

(b)    Flooding pumps were provided on each TBM and pipework was laid along the tunnels behind the machines as they progressed. Both the pumps and the pipework were sized to deal with the predicted flow through an ungrouted borehole. (Normal ingress water was taken away by a separate pumping and pipework system.)

186    During the project, although the ground on the UK side was extremely wet in certain sections, no uncontrolled flooding occurred.

**Shakespeare Cliff lower site – The sea wall**

187    As well as providing a means of access for materials to construct the UK tunnels, the lower site at Shakespeare Cliff was also used to deposit the excavated spoil from the workings. To accomplish this, a sea wall was progressively constructed with spoil being laid down by conveyor behind it. During the course of this work, a fatal accident occurred on 21 April 1990.

188    The circumstances were that normally ingressing sump water from the tunnels was deposited into settlement lagoons behind the sea wall before discharge to sea. Pipes to carry the water were laid on brackets bolted to the vertical face of the lower sea wall and were extended with the sea wall as it was lengthened. Initially, pipes had been specified in glass reinforced epoxy resin (GRE), but problems with puncturing of this pipework caused TLJV to decide to use steel pipes instead. A 6 m length of steel pipe weighing 260 kg was being fitted by Mr Stephen Wright, a plumber from the plant department, who was working with a second man.

189    The method of work involved slinging the pipe section using a two-legged chain sling fitted with 'C' hooks in each end of the pipe and attached to a lorry-mounted crane. The pipe was lifted over the sea wall, laid in brackets and loosely clamped in place. One chain leg was removed and the second leg was used to support the pipe while it was butted to the end of the existing pipe run so that a seal could be made and then the top clamp was tightened. On the day of the accident, top clamps were not fitted before the particular pipe section was butted up, and it fell from its bracket onto Mr Wright, causing fatal injuries.

190    HSE subsequently prosecuted TLJV for failing to ensure a safe system of work. TLJV pleaded not guilty and at a committal hearing at Dover Magistrates' Court in June 1991 the magistrates dismissed the case.

191    However, there were a number of points which arose from the investigation and TLJV subsequently took the following action:

(a)    Much lighter GRE pipes were used instead of steel. The problem of punctures was addressed by using a fine grain infill in the general area of the pipes.

(b)    Nylon straps were used instead of chain slings. With these straps, the weight of the pipe could be held by the lorry-mounted crane until the joint with the adjacent pipe was completed. When chains were used, one leg had to be removed from the end of the pipe before coupling could take place.

(c)    Instructions were given to secure the top clamps into position before the straps were removed.

(d)    As a separate issue, edge protection was provided at the edge of the lower sea wall platform where this work went on as there was a 3 m fall into the water of the lagoon. Employees had been wearing life-vests.

192    There was also a design issue in that the brackets used to hold the pipes were designed for GRE pipework within a tunnel. To allow access to the rear bolts to secure the top clamps, the lower bracket was tilted forward so that the pipes sat in a shallow depression rather than in a substantial curve. In addition, as the steel pipes were more rigid than GRE pipes, the latter required careful positioning on the brackets so as to be properly aligned.

**Summary of health and safety issues for general tunnelling safety**

- Access through TBMs needs to be considered at the design stage to allow both for means of escape in case of emergency and to prevent slips, trips and falls. It is important that good storage arrangements are made for extra materials, eg grout, in the event of bad ground conditions.

- Access walkways and platforms are essential for large-scale NATM-supported excavations and need to be considered at the planning stage.

- Barriers to prevent access at or near machinery are recommended where there is risk of trapping by movement, slewing or entrapment by tunnelling attachments.

- General safe access in tunnels should be planned taking into account transport (Chapter 10) and conditions underfoot; in particular, suitable walkways and hand-holds are necessary.

- Thorough surveys should be carried out to reduce the risk of flooding and collapse.

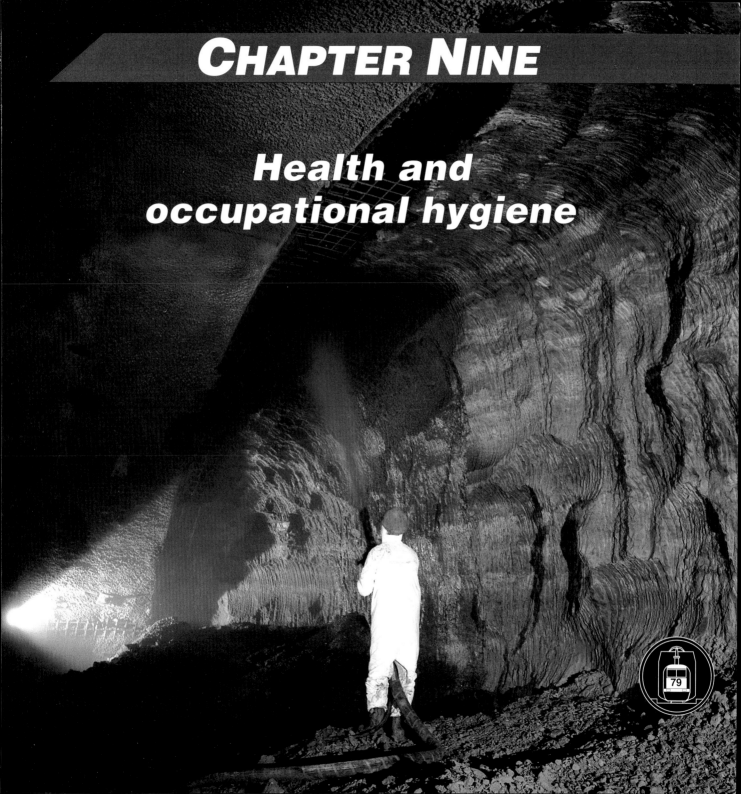

# CHAPTER NINE

# Health and occupational hygiene

79

## Introduction

193    Construction workers are exposed to numerous health hazards including harmful agents such as dusts, fumes and gases, and also to physical dangers such as noise, heat and vibration. They may be more susceptible to adverse health effects, eg to the symptoms caused by exposure to sensitising agents, owing to previous contact. When these exposures occur in tunnel workings, the possible risks to health are aggravated by the enclosed, often hot, environment. The atmosphere may also be very humid and, in marine tunnels, there will be some ingress of salt water.

## Occupational health provision

194    The Channel Tunnel project took a significant step forward in the development of occupational health management in the construction industry by setting up an in-house occupational health service based on a well-staffed and well-equipped medical centre which was controlled by an occupational health doctor. The first of the two doctors appointed, a recently retired Senior Employment Medical Adviser with HSE, drew up an occupational health service policy which was updated by his successor. The key elements of the policy were:

(a)    provision of an on-site accident and emergency service;

(b)    pre-employment medical screening for all potential underground employees;

(c)    periodic health assessments of groups of employees who were either carrying out particular tasks or exposed to certain hazardous substances;

(d)    development of a health education programme and minor treatment service.

195    The on-site accident and emergency service was a 24-hour operation and the roles and duties of the medical team were well defined. For example, for a single casualty call-out, once the medical centre nurse or doctor (if on duty) was given information about the casualty's injuries by the first-aid employee on the spot, a decision was made either to send a team of one nurse and an ambulance driver to the accident area or to evacuate the casualty. A very detailed protocol was drawn up for a multiple casualty call-out. During the course of the project, the effectiveness of call-outs was evaluated and the medical team concluded that this service was valuable in minimising long-term injury and illness.

196    Pre-employment medical examinations were carried out on all underground workers which included a health questionnaire, weight and blood pressure checks, urinalysis, and assessment of vision and hearing. Surface workers only completed a health questionnaire.

197 A number of practical difficulties appeared, as time progressed, with the vision and hearing assessments. For example, it proved difficult to stipulate what degree of hearing loss would be acceptable for employment underground as many experienced tunnellers were already suffering from existing hearing loss caused by their previous employment. It was also not practicable to carry out audiometry tests at regular intervals on all workers and very few workers had them before leaving the project. Also, in the early stages of the project, there was no formal way of correlating noise levels at work with audiometric results. Audiometry can assist in a total noise reduction programme, but only if properly introduced from the outset, with a clear understanding of its role.

198 Standards to be achieved in eyesight tests were higher for locomotive drivers, banksmen and others helping with underground locomotive movements than for those engaged in other tunnelling activities (see Chapter 10). However, even as late in the project as 1992, the difficulty in ensuring that visual assessments were properly carried out and that line management was aware of the results of them was demonstrated by the fatal accident to Mr David Griffiths. Mr Griffiths was killed when he was crushed between two trains while acting as a banksman in October 1992 (described in detail in Chapter 10, paragraphs 274 to 278). Investigation revealed that Mr Griffiths was effectively monocular, that is he had extremely poor vision in one eye. While TLJV had relaxed eyesight requirements for general underground workers, which may have permitted Mr Griffiths to carry out a non-railway job underground, they had not ensured that line management were aware of those workers with poor eyesight and that those individuals did not carry out jobs for which they were not medically fit.

199 In addition to those operating the railway, certain other groups of workers underwent periodic health assessments. These included members of the TLJV rescue team (who had annual medical examinations), those working in confined spaces, those exposed to oils, cement workers and grouters and underground toilet cleaners. These last two categories are more specifically examined later in this chapter.

200 The medical team took a positive approach to general health education. The opportunity of seeing workers on a regular basis permitted discussion of general health and the provision of general information on better health care. This was an approach strongly supported by the senior TLJV management team who took the view that an improvement in the general health of employees could lead to more productive work as well as to a reduced risk of accidents.

## Cement dermatitis

201 The Channel Tunnel project employed large numbers of workers who handled cement and, in particular, grout which was injected behind the tunnel linings. There were about 800

grouters employed in the period January 1990 to January 1992. Wet cement is an irritant to the skin, both because of its abrasive nature and its alkalinity and can cause irritant contact dermatitis. Ordinary cement has a pH of about 12, grout of about 13 and shotcrete, used in NATM, has a pH of more than 13.5. Cement causes caustic burns and, because of the presence of chromate, it can also cause chromate allergic dermatitis.

202    In the period January 1990 to January 1992, a study was made of the skin problems associated with the use of cement and the results were published in the *Journal of Occupational Medicine* in February 1994. The paper, entitled 'Cement dermatitis in underground workers during construction of the Channel Tunnel' was prepared by four authors including Dr R J Rycroft, a consultant dermatologist, both to TLJV and to HSE. In the two-year period, 1138 men with skin problems were seen at TLJV's Medical Centre and 332 of these were diagnosed as having occupational dermatitis. The total number of grouters assessed was 466, of whom 111 had a history of occupational dermatitis. Skin patch tests carried out on 86 grouters showed allergy to chromate in 56.

203    The positive aspect of this was that medical help could be given to these affected workers. Only three men had to change occupation because of their skin disease. The study paper identified steps in prevention of cement dermatitis as follows:

(a)    education of workers about the nature of cement dermatitis and burns;

(b)    advice about the use of clean protective clothing;

(c)    instruction as to the importance of washing off cement or grout spills immediately;

(d)    advice about the damaging effect on the skin of degreasing hand cleansers.

204    In the Channel Tunnel project, petroleum jelly-based hand cleaners and solvents were replaced by less hazardous materials. Employees were also advised to apply emollients to their skin to counteract the dehydrating effect of cement.

205    The study paper also points out that there was fear among employees that they would lose their jobs if they admitted to skin problems. The study demonstrated that, by taking positive action which did not threaten livelihood, this major problem of cement dermatitis could be significantly alleviated.

## Dusts, including shotcreting and use of respiratory protective equipment

206    The use of machines for rock drilling, excavation and spoil handling, as well as hand tunnelling activities and the impact of rock debris on the ground, all generated airborne dust.

While the natural dampness of the rock and water ingress had some dust suppressant effect, damp dust on clothing and machines dried out as movement took place and also gave rise to airborne dust.

### *Ventilation*

207    Local exhaust ventilation was not a practical control measure for most tunnelling operations. General extraction ventilation was feasible using large diameter ducting as close as possible to the working area. In some positions this was assisted by fans (air movers) which effectively blew dust-laden air towards the extraction ports.

208    There were limitations to the use of this control measure. The ducting used to draw air away from the face had to be raised and secured out of the way of workers and machines, yet it had to be as close to the area of work as possible.  The ducting also had to be capable of being extended as the face progressed. It was not possible to use water sprays as a dust control measure because of the low water content at which the rock and dust became a slurry.

209    In 1988, HSE carried out measurements of dust in air during construction of adit A2. The levels of airborne dust measured without effective general extraction ventilation are summarised below:

| Type of dust (milligrams per cubic metre ($mg/m^3$)) | Measurement | Occupational exposure standard (OES) |
|---|---|---|
| Total dust | up to 82 $mg/m^3$ | 10 $mg/m^3$ |
| Respirable dust | up to 26 $mg/m^3$ | 5 $mg/m^3$ |
| Respirable silica | up to 0.26 $mg/m^3$ | 0.4 $mg/m^3$ (also the maximum exposure limit) |

Note: These values are not 8-hour average exposures, but the OES is quoted to put the results in context.

210    With general extraction ventilation the measured levels of airborne dust were:

| | |
|---|---|
| Total dust | up to 24 $mg/m^3$ |
| Respirable dust | up to 12 $mg/m^3$ |
| Respirable silica | up to 0.35 $mg/m^3$ |

211　These two sets of results are not directly comparable, because they were carried out at different times under different conditions.

### Silica

212　The Channel Tunnel was driven through chalk marl, a rock which was not immediately recognisable as silica-bearing. Analysis of bulk samples gave free crystalline silica contents of 4%, 10% and 8%. The airborne dust measurements given above indicate that levels not far from the maximum exposure limit were reached. It is therefore also essential to carry out analysis for free crystalline silica of rock even where it may not be readily anticipated.

### Shotcreting

213　One of the essential features of NATM (see paragraph 178), which was employed for the construction of the UK crossover, TBM build chambers and construction adit, is shotcreting, which gives rise to high concentrations of dust in air. Briefly, this operation consists of a dry mix of carefully graded sand, aggregate and cement being blown from bulk to a hand-held spray gun. Water containing a dissolved setting accelerator is also pumped to the gun. The water and dry mix are in intimate contact as they leave the nozzle of the gun and this spray mix is directed to where it is needed at the rock face, usually several metres away. By the time it arrives at the face, it is already setting and adheres readily. In this way the desired depth of concrete is built up.

214　Shotcreting is a variable operation. It can last for just a minute or two to give a shallow depth to stabilise a small area of exposed rock face or it may last for 20 to 60 minutes to give a final thick depth over a large area after reinforcing lattice girder work is installed. Because the best mode of application is directly towards the face, the operator is subject to considerable rebounding material (although it is only a very small proportion of the shotcrete applied).

215　The levels of airborne dust to which the operator may be exposed depend upon the distances between the hand-held nozzle and the face to which the shotcrete is applied, and upon the angle of application, as much as on any general extraction control measure. Airborne levels measured were:

Total dust　　　　　up to 89 mg/m$^3$

Respirable dust　　　up to 35 mg/m$^3$

Respirable silica　　up to 0.2 mg/m$^3$

216   The low respirable silica levels were due to the careful grading of the sand used in the mix. As in the case of the figures in paragraph 209, these values are not the 8-hour average exposures of operators. The pattern of shotcrete operations made it difficult to calculate such values, especially as, when not shotcreting, the operator might be resting (with low dust exposures) or doing other work.

## *Respiratory protective equipment*

217   The other measure used as well as general extraction ventilation to protect operators against dust was the use of respiratory protective equipment. TLJV provided disposable respirators with a protection factor of ten times the exposure limits of the dusts concerned. However, studies at other tunnelling projects involving bores of smaller diameter have revealed concentrations of total dust in air of 300 mg/m$^3$, with 20 mg/m$^3$ of respirable dust. It may be that disposable respirators are not suitable when such extremely high concentrations of dust are met. It is therefore essential that adequate site-specific assessments are carried out to enable the correct respirator to be selected.

## Diesel engine exhaust emissions (diesel fumes)

218   Work in the Channel Tunnel necessitated the increasing use of diesel engines for motive power and for generators. In 1991, the Channel Tunnel Trackwork Group (CTTG), who laid the standard gauge railway, introduced a large number of extra diesel engines into the running tunnels to move their trains and these included some very large diesel-powered locomotives.

219   Diesel fumes, more correctly referred to as diesel engine exhaust emissions, contain carbon dioxide, carbon monoxide, oxides of nitrogen, particulate matter and solvent soluble matter as a variable mixture. The composition of the mixture depends on the engine load and its efficiency. The solvent soluble materials are a wide range of organic compounds which give the characteristic diesel exhaust smell and which some people find irritating to the eyes and throat.

220   HSE accepts the conclusions of the Department of Health's Committee on Carcinogenicity that exposure to diesel fumes can be associated with an increased risk of cancer, but that in most cases the risk is low. The carcinogenic risk is associated with the particulate matter in the exhaust emissions, to which the solvent soluble materials adhere.

221   At the time of writing there is no occupational exposure standard for diesel fumes, nor is there a specific method for the sampling and analysis of these fumes. Work is currently going

85

on in HSE to seek to devise such a method and this subject is being discussed by the Advisory Committee on Toxic Substances.

222    Oxides of nitrogen in diesel fumes were known at the outset of the Channel Tunnel project to present a major health concern. However, monitoring of exhaust emissions by HSE during 1992 showed concentrations of nitrogen oxides, as well as of carbon monoxide, to be well below the occupational exposure level.

223    The concentration of diesel exhaust total particulate and solvent soluble material in the air were also measured and found to be:

Total particulate    $1.04 - 3.85$ mg/m$^3$

Solvent solubles    $0.18 - 0.64$ mg/m$^3$

224    The highest values were obtained inside the passenger carriage of the marine running tunnel concreting train during transit and also outside this wagon during the uphill return journey to the surface.

225    The lowest values were obtained when the train was stationary with the locomotives shut down. The pattern of the results showed that, even away from the locality of diesel engines under load, the concentration of total particulates and solvent soluble materials in air was 1.5 to 3.0 mg/m$^3$ and 0.3 to 0.6 mg/m$^3$ respectively, with increasing concentrations downwind of the general tunnel ventilation.

226    During preparations by CTTG to use the concrete trains in the tunnels, the diesel engines were fitted with exhaust treatment units (ETUs) as exhaust cleaning equipment. The operating principles of these units are described in Chapter 5 in paragraph 101. The fires which occurred in the charcoal body of the units (see paragraph 102) led to their being withdrawn pending additional development work (see paragraph 103) and it was only towards the end of the project that they were put back into use. However, their use was an important step in addressing the reduction of pollutants caused by the operation of diesel equipment underground.

227    The health effects of diesel fumes with regard to the particulate matter in the fumes is, at the time of writing, still under consideration by HSE and others. Positive conclusions which can be drawn were:

(a) The use of catalytic converters for the diesel engines and the general tunnel ventilation reduced the concentration of carbon monoxide to below the occupational exposure standard.

(b) The general ventilation of the tunnel reduced the concentrations of oxides of nitrogen to below exposure values.

(c) General tunnel ventilation reduced the concentration of diesel exhaust total particulates and solvent soluble material but spread them throughout the tunnel.

(d) The provision of exhaust cleaning equipment would be desirable provided it was properly introduced and maintained.

**Thermal environment**

228 During underground operations there were numerous sources of heat including:

(a) the natural heat of rock and of ingressing water;

(b) heat from the setting of concrete, grout and similar substances (exothermic reactions);

(c) dissipated heat from roadheaders, spoil wagons and rock drills;

(d) dissipated heat from electrical substations, lights, power cables and motors;

(e) dissipated heat from locomotives;

(f) frictional heat produced by rock cutting.

229 Heat was removed from the tunnels by the movement of spoil to the surface, the pumping out of water and by the outflow of ventilation air, although a lot of the heat was simply transferred from one place to another (thus making the temperature more even throughout the workings). These means of removing heat, however, had little beneficial cooling effect at the source of heat production.

230 The effect of working at raised temperatures varies from discomfort to life threatening. Normal temperature may be defined as that at which a person feels comfortable. More severe conditions lead to health effects which, at the extreme, cause heat stroke because the body

cannot maintain its normal deep body temperature. This heat stress is promoted by raised air temperature, high humidity, low air velocity and high work rates of the exposed person. The effect of these factors is complex and there are a number of standards. It should be mentioned that there were no reported incidents of heat stroke among TLJV's workforce.

231    However, measurements carried out by HSE at the UK crossover in June 1990 indicated ambient temperatures of up to 30°C. While there are somewhat different methods of measuring in several international standards, the general results showed that the thermal environment in the UK crossover was uncomfortable at the time the measurements were taken and that remedial action was required. Advice given included:

(a)    Rest cabins were in the wrong place and were hotter inside than the area outside them. These should be moved to cool locations and openings provided to allow free air movement through them.

(b)    Adequate rest breaks taken in cooler areas should be allowed.

(c)    If heavy or very heavy work is necessary, more rest breaks should be taken, or more workers used to allow rotation of the task.

(d)    Spot coolers should be maintained in working condition (on the day of the measurements these were not operational).

(e)    Cooler air from the chillers should be introduced as close as possible to the working areas.

(f)    A supply of cold drinking water should be made available.

(g)    It was important that only physically fit and acclimatised people should work in the crossover carrying out high work-load jobs.

**Water ingress**

232    Analysis of the water ingressing into the Channel Tunnel through the chalk marl clay strata was carried out from time to time both by TLJV and by HSE. This did not reveal any problems of dissolved flammable and toxic gases in the Channel Tunnel project although sampling in other unrelated projects has indicated the presence of methane, carbon dioxide, organic compounds and high levels of sulphate ions giving acidic water.

## Noise

233   In any major tunnelling project, a large amount of plant and equipment is used which can create high noise levels such as air compressors, pneumatic hand tools, rock drills, ventilation fans and earth moving machinery. The first requirement under the Noise at Work Regulations 1989 is to reduce noise at source, which should occur at the planning stage. However, while some efforts were made in the Channel Tunnel project to follow this through, hearing conservation relied mainly on the wearing of hearing protection by the workers. This was not fully effective and demonstrated that an integrated policy for noise control should be provided in a tunnelling project.

234   Measurements by HSE in 1988 showed that noise levels during the initial underground work ranged from 88 to 117 dB(A). In 1990, noise measurements carried out at the UK crossover showed exposure levels in the range of 90 to 102 dB(A), from the extensive hand tunnelling typically 101 to 112 dB(A), and in locations where shotcreting was being applied the range was up to 109 dB(A). Noise levels during typical manriding train journeys could be between 75 to 100 dB(A), resulting in the personal exposure of a manrider driver of approximately 95 dB(A). At this time TLJV made arrangements to train members of the safety department in noise competency, including use of noise measuring equipment.

235   TLJV then arranged for additional noise assessments to be carried out which resulted in implementation of the following noise exposure reduction methods:

(a)   selection of suitable hearing protection;

(b)   training in and supervision of the use of hearing protection;

(c)   designation of hearing protection zones;

(d)   improved means of informing workers of the risk of noise induced hearing loss via field safety talks, poster campaigns and mess room/canteen television safety bulletins.

236   As subsequent noise assessments became progressively more comprehensive, it became evident that some of the engineering control measures identified to reduce noise exposure could not be pursued because at this stage it was too late to incorporate them into the machinery concerned.

237    Because of the relative lack of engineering control of noise source, reliance was placed on the need for an effectively supervised hearing protection programme. This led initially to all underground workings being designated as ear protection zones, including those areas where noise levels were not excessive. This policy was difficult to enforce by TLJV and eventually a more discerning approach was introduced, based on zoning related to specific activities, including mobile zones for activities passing through quiet workings.

238    There were also instances where engineering noise control measures should have been applied before equipment was brought into use. Simple examples included the provision of silencers to exhaust systems of diesel generators. Even improved procurement systems which included pre/post purchasing noise emission monitoring still allowed unsilenced equipment to be brought onto site as late as 1992.

## Infectious diseases

239    Provision of adequate and clean toilet facilities is essential to tunnelling operations. Even more important is the protection of those who clean and remove toilets. HSE made specific visits to ensure that the control of hygiene operatives' health was satisfactory.

240    TLJV's occupational health service policy sought to protect the underground toilet cleaners who were exposed to formaldehyde as well as to potential contamination with human excrement. Formaldehyde is a skin sensitiser and occasionally can be a pulmonary sensitiser. Pre-employment and six-monthly screening was provided for this group of workers and consisted of skin assessment, spirometry and a respiratory questionnaire. Guidelines on personal hygiene and correct working practices were also reinforced. Of particular significance was the full immunisation programme for the toilet cleaners against poliomyelitis, typhoid and tetanus. These steps are essential for people carrying out this work.

## First aid provision

241    TLJV provided a very large number of trained first aiders for the underground works. With the distances involved, it was important that a trained first aider was quickly on hand who was able to carry out emergency treatment and who could also make an assessment of the condition of the injured or sick person. At TBMs and other work locations, advanced certificate first-aid personnel were provided who were able to administer oxygen and nitrous oxide from sets kept at these locations.

## Health risk assessments

242  TLJV developed a number of methods of carrying out health risk assessments under the Control of Substances Hazardous to Health Regulations (COSHH). From time to time, inspectors found that substances which were in use either did not have risk assessments or that these were inadequate. However major efforts were made by TLJV, and later by sub-contractors, to ensure that risk assessments were available, which included the appointment of an occupational hygienist by TLJV in 1990.

## Summary of health and occupational hygiene issues

- The provision of an occupational health service was a major benefit to the Channel Tunnel project.

- Cement dermatitis was more effectively controlled by education, health surveillance and monitoring.

- Creation of dusts during tunnelling was significant and conclusions reached were:

  - High levels during excavation were controlled by carefully managed general extraction ventilation, which considerably reduced airborne dust levels.

  - Respirable silica was present. Sampling and analysis help to ensure that control measures are in place and adequate.

  - Suitable respiratory protective equipment should be provided and worn.

  - Shotcreting may require a higher standard of respiratory protective equipment dependent on the concentrations measured.

- For diesel engine exhaust emissions (diesel fumes), catalytic converters on engines and general tunnel ventilation can reduce the concentration of carbon monoxide and oxides of nitrogen to below occupational exposure standard values. Further controls such as exhaust scrubbing equipment should be provided where reasonably practicable to reduce these gases, as well as particulate matters in the air.

- The thermal environment needs to be controlled to reduce heat stress by a combination of control measures, working practices, engineering methods and, possibly, health surveillance.

- Ventilation systems need to be designed in advance of construction to take account of the assessment of concentrations of flammable and asphyxiant gases and of airborne hazardous substances as well as considering the thermal environment in the tunnel during construction.

- Noise presents a significant hazard in tunnelling:

  - A policy for noise control should be in place which includes the appointment of noise competent people to carry out assessments and to take corrective action.

  - All potential noise producing machinery and equipment for use on site should be examined beforehand to ensure that noise levels generated are as low as reasonably practicable.

  - Hearing protectors should be provided and used in remaining areas where there are unavoidable high noise levels, and this should be backed up by a programme of education for workers.

- Adequate and clean toilet facilities should be provided underground and it is particularly important that those cleaning toilets are fully protected.

- Underground first aid provision is essential to reduce the effects of injury or ill health.

- Relevant health risk assessments are required for the Control of Substances Hazardous to Health Regulations 1994 (COSHH).

94

A construction locomotive pulling a spoil train

in one of the running tunnels

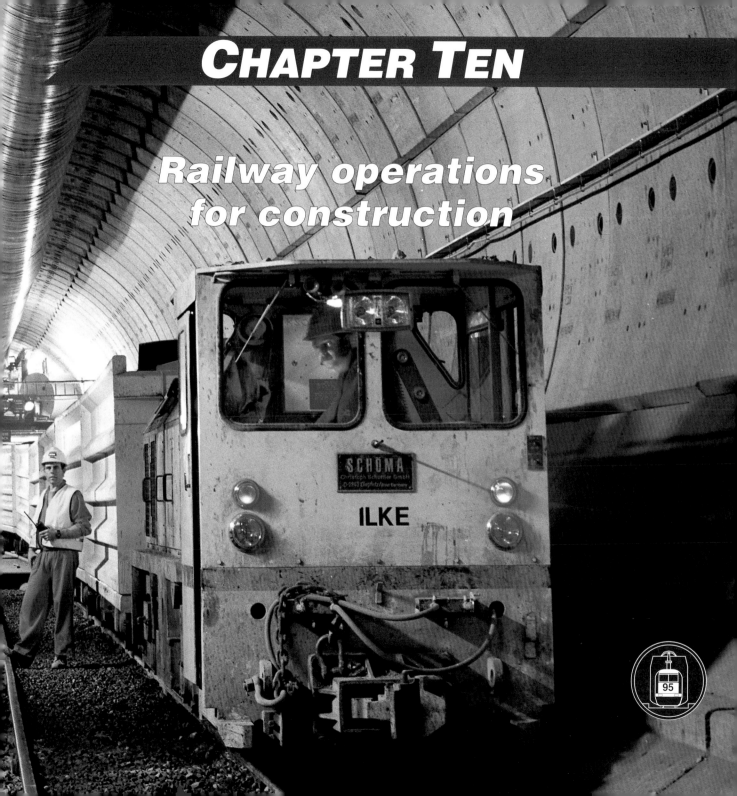

# CHAPTER TEN

## Railway operations for construction

## Introduction

243    The use of the construction gauge and, later, the standard gauge railways throughout the Channel Tunnel project was crucial to its completion. Rail operations presented a hazard which, unless properly managed, could result in a high risk of serious injury. Three fatal accidents in the UK sector were caused by rail activities and there were a number of other rail incidents, several of which had potential for multiple casualties. This chapter describes the railways and key technical and managerial health and safety issues.

## Description of the railways

244    The construction gauge (900 mm between rails) railway was the sole transportation system for workers and materials during most of the tunnelling phase of the project. On both sides of the Channel, TML decided to centre their tunnelling operations some kilometres away from the location of the portals of the completed fixed link. Shakespeare Cliff, between Folkestone and Dover, was the starting point for the UK tunnels. At the bottom of the cliff there was a shelf jutting out into the sea which became known as Shakespeare Cliff lower site. The narrow gauge construction railway was laid from here both inland to the terminal site and towards France to the undersea border and all trains and construction materials entered the tunnel system here using an inclined tunnel or adit. These can be seen in Figure 3.

245    All the UK tunnel drives started at Shakespeare Cliff. The construction gauge railway was laid on the lower site in the initial period down adit A1 and when adit A2 was completed, it was switched from A1 to A2. Two pairs of tracks were then laid in each tunnel. There was a major marshalling area (known as the 'pit bottom') at the bottom of the adit (A2) and trains were routed through the six tunnel drives at this point.

246    As the TBMs extended each tunnel drive, the construction gauge railway lines were progressively laid behind them. At the height of the operations in the UK there were over 180 km of construction railway with 180 sets of points and crossings, and at that time the Channel Tunnel UK construction railway was the third largest rail system in Britain after British Rail and the London Underground. There were 150 locomotives and many more segment-carrying flat cars, materials cars and manriders in addition to muck wagons. Nearly 500 drivers were rostered on four shifts, with one rest shift.

247    Train drivers and the controllers communicated by radio. The marshalling area (pit bottom) was the only place where a visual light signalling system was used. TLJV decided very early in the contract not to make general use of a visual signalling system because it would be

susceptible to breakdown in the harsh and changing tunnel conditions. Instead, a system of radio communication between train drivers and a central controller (known as the Operations Board Controller or OBC) was introduced, backed up by local control of train movements by a trained employee known as a person-in-charge (PIC). The principle of this system was acceptable to the Railway Inspectorate.

248   A general speed limit of 30 km per hour was imposed. Substantially lower speed limits were set at certain areas, eg when passing stationary work locations on the adjacent track.

249   From 1991 onwards, work began in the two running tunnels to lay the single track standard gauge (1.435 m) railway which is the passenger and freight transport system of the operating railway. The UK terminal was also laid with standard gauge track. The major task of fitting out the underground workings meant that the standard gauge railway also had to be used for construction activities while it was being installed. The same control system as for the narrow gauge railway was used, that is, radio control between a central control point (here known as the Rail Movement Control) and the driver. Local control was again provided by a person-in-charge.

**Design and maintenance of equipment**

250   In December 1987, four empty Mulhauser spoil wagons weighing 8 tonnes each ran away down adit A1 after a coupling had failed. They were being taken down the adit by a Hunslet rack locomotive which was at the back of the train. Four of the wagons broke away from the fifth spoil wagon and ran 300 m down the track of the A1 before derailing and causing considerable damage. There were several minor injuries to workers who had to get out of the way. The HSE investigation revealed that:

(a)   the keep plates and bolts retaining the coupling of the wagon which broke away were missing. The coupling was left attached to the wagon remaining at the top of the adit;

(b)   no secondary coupling chains were provided between the wagons, nor was there proper provision to attach such chains;

(c)   two of the brake shoes were missing from the wagon which broke away;

(d)   the driver had been instructed to place the locomotive behind the spoil wagons, so that the braking effect of the locomotive was not available to the wagons. This was because of perceived difficulties with recharging the battery of the locomotive should this be necessary while the train was in the tunnel. (There was a shortage of charged batteries.);

(e)     although there were planned maintenance schedules for all rolling stock, maintenance had not started.

251     TLJV took action to deal with points (a) to (e). It was particularly important to begin a planned maintenance programme and to ensure that secondary couplings were provided for wagons. This incident occurred at the very beginning of tunnelling on completion of the erection of the marine service tunnel TBM and it again emphasises the need to ensure, before production begins, that design factors are carefully examined and that maintenance programmes are in place.

252     The five constituent companies of TLJV were prosecuted by HSE following this runaway incident. While there were no serious injuries, there was clearly potential for a major accident, and informations were laid under the Health and Safety at Work etc Act 1974 and Construction Regulations that the spoil wagon was not maintained.

253     The locomotive maintenance workshops which were subsequently constructed at Shakespeare Cliff lower site were engaged in one of the largest non-tunnelling activities which took place throughout most of the lifetime of the project. These workshops ensured that maintenance was provided for railway equipment and that design modifications were carried out as required.

## Pedestrian access through the tunnels

254     A number of access matters were considered in Chapter 8. This section deals specifically with pedestrian use of the tunnels while trains operated. Throughout the phases of the project, consideration had to be given to ways of preventing workers being struck by moving trains. Unfortunately, on three occasions men were struck and died and there were important lessons to be learned from these accidents.

255     The first fatality in the Channel Tunnel UK project happened on 23 January 1989. Mr Andrew McKenna was walking in the marine service tunnel when he was struck by a laden train. The tunnels were generally well lit and at that time, TLJV had not stipulated that personnel in the tunnels must wear high-visibility clothing and so he was not wearing this. The driver of the train failed to see Mr McKenna until it was too late to stop. There was another train in the vicinity going in the opposite direction. The exact circumstances which led to Mr McKenna's death were never satisfactorily established.

256   TLJV's actions after the accident were:

(a)   the issue of high-visibility clothing with a mandatory requirement for it to be worn underground;

(b)   better control of pedestrian entry to the tunnel systems with more closely monitored use of permits, particularly for those workers such as Mr McKenna, whose job as an engineer's assistant necessitated his entering the tunnel at times other than at a shift change, when manriding trains were used;

(c)   the induction training given to all site personnel included more on rail safety awareness;

(d)   the placing of redesigned pedestrian refuges in the tunnel;

(e)   TLJV issued the 'General Operating Procedures' for rail transport in one volume for the first time;

(f)   the introduction of further speed restrictions; for a short time the overall speed limit was reduced to 20 km per hour.

257   The increasing lengths of all the drives as the project progressed meant that use of manriding trains became the normal way of travelling underground. However, there was always a requirement for walking in the tunnels and practices were introduced or altered as follows:

(a)   It was essential to be seen, hence the importance of high-visibility clothing.

(b)   A system of sound signals was reinforced for moving trains so that personnel were aware of the direction in which a train was travelling as it is often extremely difficult to be sure of a train's direction of approach in a tunnel.

(c)   The procedure also required that pedestrians should stand back or use a refuge and signal an acknowledgement to the driver before the train passed.

(d)   For temporary workplaces on or near the track, flagmen were employed to signal trains past that area.

(e)   As a further measure, when standard gauge trains operated in the running tunnels, telephone permission had to be obtained from the controller before anyone was allowed to enter the tunnel on foot and train drivers regularly reported any unauthorised personnel in the tunnel.

## Moving trains into TBMs

258    Trains delivering materials to TBMs had to be breasted (that is, the locomotive was at the rear of the train and pushed the rolling stock) under the gantries of the machine for a considerable distance to reach unloading points. This had to be done because of the height of the locomotive and the consequent lack of clearance to lift materials over it from the flatbed cars. Breasting of trains is an extremely hazardous operation as, in addition to the normal confines of the tunnel, the framework of the TBM gantries significantly reduced clearances between the train and the TBM. Also personnel working on the TBM would often need to gain access onto the track during this operation for a variety of reasons.

259    TLJV recognised that breasting trains into TBMs posed a considerable hazard if it was not adequately controlled and drew up a procedure so that a banksman guided the train into the TBM. The banksman communicated with the train driver by radio and either walked along the TBM walkway or rode on the front end of the train to guide him.

260    The railway serving the TBM in the marine running tunnel south became twin track for the first time late in 1989, resulting in a need for more drivers. Some banksmen became drivers and were not replaced. From time to time after that, trains breasted into the TBM without banksmen which contributed to a fatal accident on 10 January 1990.

261    A segment train was entering the TBM in a breasting mode without a banksman. Mr Keith Lynch, a grouter on the TBM, had been picking up discarded grout plugs from the invert of the tunnel for re-use. He did not appear to see the train nor was he seen by the driver. He was struck by the train as it moved slowly into the TBM.

262    HSE insisted that TLJV take immediate steps which were:

(a)    to provide trained and properly equipped banksmen for all breasting operations into the TBM;

(b)    to issue new procedures for breasting;

(c)    to train non-rail personnel, in particular the supervisors of the TBMs and other people who controlled train activity to ensure that these procedures were well known and were monitored;

(d)    to establish a safe shunting position with emergency brake and radio communication at the front of the segment trains.

263　TLJV were prosecuted by HSE for failing to ensure the safety of employees when trains entered the TBM, and substantial fines were imposed. The evidence in this case also indicated that production needs were given priority over safety. Previously there had been a second person available for breasting operations but when the second person was removed to provide extra drivers for other trains, there were occasions when no one acted as a banksman. TLJV had recognised this problem but had not taken enough action to deal with it. It is important that arrangements are in place to guide trains safely into areas where there is limited space, not only when entering TBMs but when travelling through or past other fixed or moving structures or equipment.

## Transport of personnel by train

264　The Channel Tunnel project had to make provision for the major logistical exercise of transporting people to their places of work throughout the system every day. Special manriding vehicles were used from the early days, but the increase in the number of workers involved meant that manriding trains became necessary. These trains consisted of manriding cars with driver's cabs at either end of the train. Several examples illustrate safety problems.

**Figure 6**　Manriding train

265　Early in the project, the access openings in the sides of the manriding cars were fitted only with a guard-rail. This presented a hazard either of someone accidentally placing a part of the body outside the opening and being struck by another train or fixed equipment, or of someone falling out through the opening. An employee travelling on a manriding train suffered a broken leg after it was struck by fixed equipment in the tunnel. TLJV fitted the openings in manriders with webbing infill attached to the guard-rails which had to be lifted up and then fell back into place (see Figure 6).

## Braking of trains

266    In the earlier part of this chapter, a train runaway was described, which resulted from braking and maintenance problems. There was a further incident in 1992 which could have had serious consequences, and which revealed problems concerning braking and parking procedures.

267    On 3 June 1992, two flat cars carrying full concrete remixers ('bullets'), weighing approximately 15 tonnes each, ran about 5 km down the gradient of the land service tunnel when they were uncoupled from the locomotive. They eventually reached a speed estimated to be in excess of 50 km per hour. Fortunately this happened during the night shift and the tunnel was quiet, although there were two trains on the other track.

268    When the runaway began, the driver and PIC used their radios to warn other drivers and the controller (OBC). Further along the tunnel another driver, with agreement of the OBC, placed his locomotive in the way of the runaway cars to slow down and stop them. He applied his service brake and left his locomotive. It was shunted approximately 100 m on collision, the track was torn away from the tunnel floor and there was extensive damage to the equipment.

269    The immediate cause of the incident was the failure of the train driver to connect the brake airlines from his locomotive to the rolling stock before he started the journey. Following that, he did not carry out a brake continuity test (described in the next paragraph) which was a required procedure. The trains (locomotives and rolling stock) were fitted with air-operated service brakes and air-released (ie spring-operated) parking brakes, and with no air in the rolling stock system their service brakes did not work and the parking brakes were applied by the springs. The locomotive was powerful enough to pull the train with the rolling stock parking brakes on, resulting in these wearing out rapidly. When the driver uncoupled the two cars, there was no braking effect from the rolling stock as the parking brakes had become ineffective. Finally, the PIC, who helped the driver to uncouple, failed to insert a chocking device (known as a chain chock) correctly under the wheels of the rolling stock.

270    HSE's investigation revealed that a significant number of the train drivers did not carry out adequate brake continuity tests because the operations procedure was difficult to follow. The continuity test ensured that the air brake system throughout the train was fully charged. It was considered to be necessary at any time that a train was configured, and also when any piece of rolling stock was coupled or uncoupled. There were two ways of doing the test:

(a)    The driver remained in his cab while another employee went to the rear of the train and opened the service air line at the back wagon. When the driver released the service brake, air rushed through this line. If the second man had heard escaping air then there was continuous braking.

(b)     The driver had a simple device, consisting of a plunger and a small cylinder which he connected to the end of the air line at the back of the train. On release of the service brake, air pushed the plunger up. When the driver returned to the rear of the train to check, he could see the position of the plunger.

271     What had happened in practice was that the second procedure (b) had fallen into disuse. There were times when the first procedure (a) was not followed either.

272     There was little attempt to supervise the formation of trains or the carrying out of braking procedures. HSE's view was that supervision and monitoring was essential to achieve not only the correction of faults found, but also to reinforce good behaviour.

273     HSE insisted that TLJV take action as follows:

(a)     Supervisors should check that tests were being carried out.

(b)     Drivers and banksmen (who assisted in brake tests) should be fully retrained in the test procedure.

(c)     Monitoring should also be carried out by more senior management.

(d)     Correct procedures for positioning chocking devices should be followed.

(e)     Drivers and banksmen should be reminded of their own obligations.

## Train manoeuvres in tunnels

274     Another hazard occurred when trains were manoeuvring in the tunnels, and in particular when using crossings, and when breasting on the same track or over crossings. For these operations, a trained banksman was always needed. On 6 October 1992, a fatal accident occurred to Mr David Griffiths in the marine service tunnel during train manoeuvres. He was acting as a banksman of a train known as the hygiene train.

275     The hygiene train was travelling out of the tunnel at change of shift. In order to bring out manriding trains from behind it, as the priority was to transport personnel to and from their work locations, the driver was instructed to park the train on a section of the other track. The distance between these two sets of tracks in the service tunnel was about 700 mm and the

locomotives and rolling stock overhung the tracks. To move out of the way, the hygiene train first had to travel forward across a set of points to the ingoing track and then breast back along that track to clear the points for the subsequent movement of the manriding trains, one of which then moved up the outgoing track to these points. Mr Griffiths stood between the tracks to reset the points for this manriding train to continue moving forward out of the tunnel. It started to move and at the same time the hygiene train moved backwards on the other track. He was caught by the back edge of the hygiene train's last carriage and was pushed against the second carriage of the manrider which trapped him in the small space (of less than 300 mm) between the trains.

276    HSE's investigation revealed that:

(a)    there was no effective supervision on the hygiene train for the six days prior to the accident;

(b)    Mr Griffiths had not received any training either for general underground work or, in particular, to act as a banksman for any train;

(c)    he had very poor visibility in his right eye. Underground workers were given medicals and Mr Griffiths had one in 1990. He did not pass the eyesight test and so was not permitted to work underground. However, early in 1992, this decision was changed and he was permitted to work underground to carry out general duties (but not for train operations);

(d)    the hygiene train regularly worked unsupervised by management except for the charge-hand. This man was away on leave at the time of the accident.

(e)    first and second line supervisors above the chargehand on the train had little knowledge of the safe operating procedures for the construction railway. This was a serious deficiency, and during the subsequent court proceedings, evidence was given that, because of its very low priority of track occupation compared with works trains, the hygiene train regularly carried out backward shunting manoeuvres. This train was therefore frequently involved in the highest risk activity on the railway;

(f)    there were no procedures to govern the movements of trains in opposite directions at points within the tunnels.

277  HSE required TLJV to take immediate management action with the result that:

(a)  the chief safety adviser was appointed as a railways section manager with safety as his remit;

(b)  all site personnel were retrained in railway safety procedures;

(c)  new working procedures were adopted.

278  HSE subsequently took legal proceedings against TLJV. The judge in his summary stated that there had been 'a disastrous failure of supervision' and imposed the highest fine recorded against a construction consortium.

## Trains travelling on the same track

279  On 23 November 1992, a fully-laden standard gauge train ran into the back of another in running tunnel south while the trains were being breasted, ie propelled at high speed, into their work positions. The use of work trains in the running tunnels and the long distances involved had resulted in the practice of propelling trains in, or sometimes out of the tunnel, at 30 kph. Although there were procedures for this, both these and the physical arrangements were inadequate.

280  The first train into the tunnel had made an unscheduled stop at a cross-passage. The driver of the second train was unaware of this. The shunter/banksman of the second train who was riding at the front of it failed to see the other train in advance and applied the emergency brake too late. A mess room, made from a converted shipping container resting unsecured on a flatbed rail car of this train, slid forward as a result of the impact. It trapped an employee between a structure outside the flatbed and the front guard-rail which resulted in him suffering serious injury. Several other workers sustained minor injuries.

281  HSE, TLJV and the trackwork contractors (CTTG) whose trains were involved carried out an investigation, as a result of which a whole series of technical and procedural recommendations were made. However, the key elements related to the very poor arrangements for the shunter/banksman. These were:

(a)  The cabin in which the banksman sat was 'home-made', uncomfortable (he sat sideways in it) and had a very small aperture for him to look out of.

(b)  The arrangements for communication between the driver and the banksman were inadequate, the latter having to hold the radio in one hand and the emergency brake in the other at all times.

(c)     Communications between the Rail Movement Controller (RMC) and drivers were inadequate in that the RMC gave no instructions to trains once they had proceeded into the tunnels after clearance.

282     Although a number of practical steps were taken to rectify the above deficiencies, the outcome of this incident was that procedures were adopted by TLJV to improve the management of the railways. This strengthened the action already taken following the accident to Mr Griffiths. The new railway manager worked underground for most of each day and first-line supervisors played a far more active part in safety management. It is no coincidence that, following this reorganisation, there were no further serious rail movement incidents.

**Summary of health and safety matters during operation of construction railways**

- High-visibility clothing should be worn.

- Separated walkways or, as a minimum, controlled areas are recommended.

- Good induction training will help to familiarise all personnel with transport arrangements.

- Those working underground in the vicinity of railways should have reasonable eyesight and hearing.

- Speed limits should be set.

- Headlights and taillights are necessary for locomotives and trains.

- Properly trained and equipped banksmen are necessary (it is assumed that all drivers are trained).

- Operating procedures should be written down.

- Safe shunting positions are needed for banksmen, either on the train or in the tunnel.

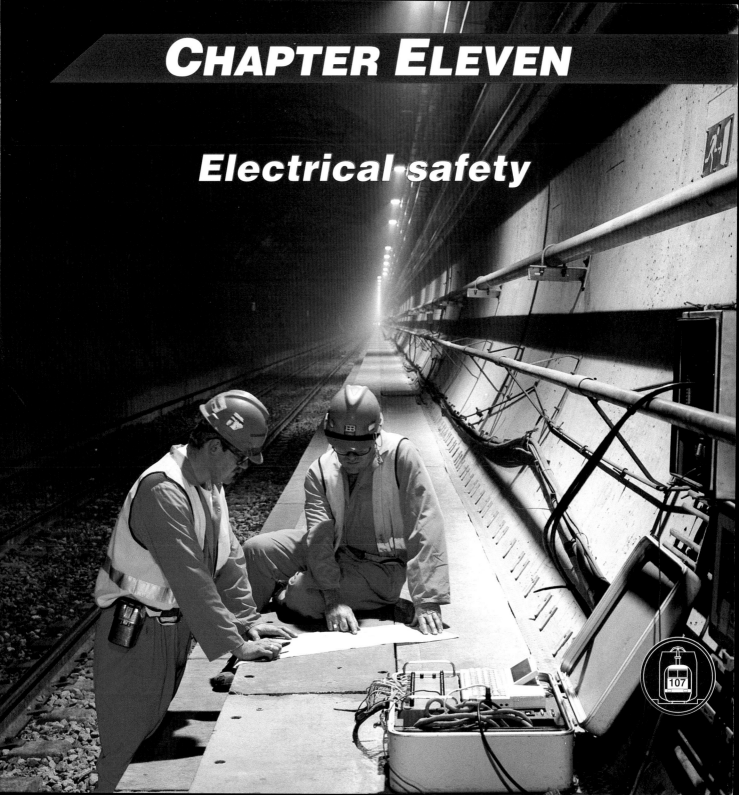

# CHAPTER ELEVEN

## Electrical safety

107

## Introduction

283　The construction phase of the Channel Tunnel involved the extensive use of electrically-powered equipment, with power needs ranging from the high demands of TBMs and the construction gauge railway electric locomotives down to 110 V portable tools. Electrical equipment had to be capable of withstanding not only the rigours of normal construction activities, but also the special demands of a major tunnelling project with the increased possibility of mechanical damage and wet conditions. TLJV recognised the high risk posed by using electrical equipment in such conditions and gave a high priority to electrical safety. In spite of this, two of the eight fatalities which occurred in the UK project were electrically related, one of them caused by electric shock and the second contributed to by a major electrical design defect and inadequate maintenance.

284　This chapter looks at the electrical systems and plant in use in the project during construction and, later in the project, during the concurrent commissioning phase. The six important elements to consider are design, selection, use, maintenance, repair and testing of electrical systems and plant. While there are numerous overlaps between these elements, the effects of each on safety will be described to illustrate its importance.

## Electrical supply to the Channel Tunnel

285　During construction, the electrical supply for the project was from incoming mains electricity transformed down to 11 kV supplies for the tunnel equipment. Each TBM was supplied by a dedicated 11 kV power supply which was transformed down to working voltages by on-board transformers. In addition, a further three cables were installed to supply power for tunnel services such as traction, pumping, ventilation and lighting. Two of these cables were laid in the service tunnel, while the other was in the running tunnel north. All of the 11 kV service cables were installed in pre-prepared lengths of 375 m fitted with mining couplings.

286　In addition, 4 megawatt (MW) diesel standby generators were installed at Shakespeare Cliff lower site to provide emergency power for essential tunnel systems such as pumps, ventilation and lighting in the event of a total failure of the 11 kV system. This was supplied by a separate emergency cable, by-passing the primary switchboard.

## Principal electrical hazards

287　The two principal electrical hazards are electric shock and/or burn, and fire caused by electrical fault. There is a third less direct result of electrical defect, that of electrical short-circuit causing dangerous movement of machinery. Both TLJV and HSE recognised the serious hazards posed by electrical fires in the confined space of the tunnels. From the outset, HSE and TLJV considered that it was a priority to ensure that equipment which provided maximum protection against these hazards was selected for use underground. This did not always occur and this chapter considers both electric shock and fire hazards, as well as abnormal movement of machinery caused by electrical defect.

## Design

288    The design of cables and equipment for use underground has been a major concern of the mining industry for many years. In the Channel Tunnel a number of the standards were applied or adapted for use. In particular, HSE and TLJV concentrated on the design of the high voltage electrical cables and other equipment.

289    Most electric cable fires are caused when the sheathing and insulation is ignited by an unrelated fire, although some are caused by excess current. The sheathing and insulation then becomes further fuel for the fire and generates significant quantities of smoke and toxic gases. Furthermore, if the cable is still live when the insulation fails, there is likely to be a flash-over with substantial electrical energy feeding into the fault, until protective devices such as fuses or circuit-breakers operate. Cable fires which arise from excess current are often the result of either mechanical damage or water absorption by plastic insulation.

290    The possibility of fires involving the main 11 kV incoming supply cables was of particular concern because these large cables presented both a significant fire loading and a possible source of ignition. A number of meetings were held between HSE and TLJV in the earlier part of the project to consider the specification of the supply cables. HSE pressed for these to comply with the relevant British Standard specifications for tunnelling electrics, in terms of resistance to abrasion, flammability of cable insulation and toxicity of resultant fumes, as well as mechanical strength and flexibility. Ultimately, no single sheath completely satisfied all criteria and the final choice was a compromise between technical performance and cost. The cabling chosen was provided with a medium-density, cross-linked polyethylene outer sheath designed for low smoke and corrosive gas emissions.

291    An electrical design defect contributed significantly to the fatal accident to Mr Woodward. The segment erector tray which trapped him moved unexpectedly when a short-circuit occurred, caused by damage to the control circuit. When this happened, the solenoid of the control circuit, which was not referenced to earth, was energised, so causing the abnormal movement.

292    The electrical deficiencies in design were:

(a)    the solenoid control system was not referenced to earth and so had the potential to fail to danger in the event of earth faults. British Standard 5304 *Safety of machinery* refers to the requirement for electrical solenoid control systems to be so referenced;

(b)    the cable, although originally in conduit, had been snagged and pulled out. Insufficient consideration had been given to protection for the cable.

293    It was also of concern that the investigation revealed a taped joint in the control cable which indicated that this problem had occurred before and should have been dealt with.

294    The fire at an underground battery charging station is described in Chapter 5. There were flaws in the design of that system which led to a serious fire incident. The remedial action, provision of DC circuit-breakers, an electrical proving system, and polarity sensing protection, should have been considered at the design stage in view of the location of the equipment.

**Selection of equipment**

*Transformers*

295    It is essential to select the correct type of transformers for use underground as they are a significant potential source of electrical fires. Unlike most electrical equipment, many types of transformer are difficult to protect adequately against the effects of electrical faults. Even when a fuse or circuit-breaker is fitted to the output side, the connection from the secondary winding to the fuse or breaker remains inadequately protected against electrical faults. Normally good design alone is relied upon to minimise the possibility of faults occurring in this 'unprotected zone'. The mining industry transformers feature interphase barriers which ensure that any fault occurring will be one to earth. Equipment can also be fitted which detects earth faults.

296    The Channel Tunnel project did not make use of mining industry transformers. The majority of transformers were however specified as 'dry', ie they contained solid resin rather than mineral oil for insulating or cooling purposes. Despite this there were a number of transformer fires arising from electrical faults. One of these is described in Chapter 5. As these transformers had different characteristics, it was not possible to establish any one common

cause of fire. For example, one fire was the result of a poor connection in a transformer winding, while another was caused by an overlong screw on a cable shroud piercing the insulation of the cable.

### *Locomotives*

297    Selection of the correct electric locomotives and electrical supply system for the construction gauge railway proved difficult in the earlier part of the project, when much of the power was electrically provided. The locomotives drew power from a 500 V DC shrouded overhead conductor. This conductor was continually added to, to keep up with the TBM as it moved forward. The locomotives had to operate under battery power over the short distance separating the live conductor from the rear of the TBM.

298    The Hunslet Mk I electric locomotives suffered a series of smoke incidents involving battery/plug connectors. This was largely due to water/dirt contamination and possible cracking of the insulation, allowing substantial current to track across the insulation, causing it to degrade and carbonise. Over time this carbonisation led to a cumulative increase in current tracking, ultimately causing overheating of the plugs and sockets. This was successfully addressed when the Mk II locomotives were introduced.

299    There were also numerous smoke incidents involving the locomotive power collection equipment. These incidents were caused by overheating resulting from relatively heavy power losses (typically 35 to 70 kW) and also from the arcing and flashing which occurred in wet areas of the tunnel. Traction currents were of the order of 600 amps (A). Such incidents normally involved a short length of the overhead conductor shrouding, and were easily dealt with. A reduction of the current density (amperage) at the collectors alleviated the problem and the shrouding was also improved so that it was better able to resist the effects of damp. Improved ventilation was also fitted to the locomotives; this was interlocked to ensure cooling fans were working before the locomotives could be used.

300    It is worth noting that while there were substantial currents in the overhead conductor system for the construction gauge railway, it was extremely well shrouded, preventing any access to the live parts. As a result, there were no reports of electric shocks from the conductor system.

*TBMs*

301    Low voltage electrical control circuitry fitted to the TBMs was to IP65 standard (splash proof), based on dry conditions encountered during the 1970s tunnelling work and the results from numerous boreholes. However, significant parts of the tunnels proved to be very wet, causing numerous failures and malfunctions of TBM control circuits. While there was no immediate risk to life from electric shock, such failures have potentially serious safety implications in terms of abnormal movement of plant or equipment. Improvements were made to equipment most prone to problems under these conditions. However, the solution would have been to select equipment suitably designed for wetter areas.

302    Wet conditions also resulted in numerous spurious trips of earth leakage circuit-breakers (ELCB) fitted to electrical equipment on TBMs. To overcome this problem, ELCB current and time ratings were set to protect the equipment. It is important to ensure that these protection devices are set at the right level to prevent electric shock.

303    TLJV adopted the usual UK system of lowest practicable voltage for low voltage electrical supply and distribution. All portable tools and equipment were supplied at reduced low voltage on the 110 V centre-tapped earth system supplied from 110 V transformers. This system and the 415 V system which supplied it were both equipped with sensitive earth leakage protection, primarily designed to protect equipment from electrical faults.

**Use of equipment**

304    An example of good control and use is reflected in the way in which the 11 kV electric cables supplying the TBMs were extended as the machines tunnelled. Each TBM was supplied directly from 11 kV feeder cables. Approximately 400 m of flexible trailing cable was stored on drums at the rear of each machine. This was paid out slowly as the TBM progressed forward, and was hung on temporary support brackets on the tunnel walls. (These high voltage drums were interlocked to prevent parallel operation.) When 375 m of trailing cable had been paid out, the power was isolated, the trailing cable was disconnected from the incoming supply and spooled back onto the drum. New corresponding lengths of fixed cable were added and reconnected to the trailing cables using mining couplers. The system was made live again, allowing the next 375 m TBM drive to commence.

305    This repeated disconnection and reconnection of the TBM power supplies was identified as a potentially high-risk activity and was controlled by a strict permit-to-work system and written electrical procedures. Again, in spite of the evident risks, no accidents were reported

which were directly associated with the TBM power supplies, although there were three or four small fires resulting from water ingress through the couplers. This was cured by using a waterproof filling compound.

## Maintenance

306    TLJV carried out specific training for electricians. This included a three-day course and an examination. Electricians had to satisfy the examining supervisors that they had the necessary training and experience. On doing so, they were appointed as 'approved' electricians. TLJV compiled their own electrical safety rules which were published and became very extensive. These were given to all electricians and set out the duties of those concerned.

307    As an additional step, in May 1990 an electrical design audit was carried out. The audit identified a number of improvements which were adopted. These included implementation of computer generation and recording of electrical maintenance schedules and work, along with a dedicated team to carry out maintenance. Monthly testing of the four standby generators was also implemented. An electrical safety office (ESO) was set up to provide all material and to compile procedures.

## Repair

308    One of the fatal accidents on the project occurred during the repair of electrical equipment. On 29 July 1990, Mr Charles McCourt, an electrician working on the TBM of the marine service tunnel, was electrocuted while working on live leads of a 415 V supply. The socket which had been attached to these leads had been pulled off its mounting by a passing train which had snagged an extension lead plugged into the socket. The bare leads of the cable of the socket were exposed and were still energised. At the time of the accident, Mr McCourt was fitting an insulated connector block to the exposed ends of the cables when he sustained a fatal electric shock. The isolation switch, which was approximately 9 m away, was not de-energised.

309    Mr McCourt had attended the electrician's course (see paragraph 306). TLJV's electrical safety rules included instructions that no one should work on any apparatus or conductors which exposed them or anyone else to danger and that electricians should ensure that electrical apparatus was isolated before working on it. This did not happen in this instance.

310    There is a general point from this which is relevant to future operations. Electrical equipment and leads can be damaged in the tunnelling environment and electricians will

naturally be involved in numerous cable repairs. It is essential that tunnel electricians, and others who see equipment which they believe to be dangerous, do not work on or touch this equipment until it is proved to be isolated.

## Testing

311    In this project, a major element of work was the testing of the electrical equipment installed for the permanent passenger railway which consisted of two major electrical systems:

(a)    the 21 kV electrical supply to seven major underground substations for all power requirements such as ventilation, lighting, pumping stations, and many mechanical systems;

(b)    the 25 kV power supply for operational passenger trains using an overhead catenary system (OCS). The wires for the OCS are located in the roof of each of the running tunnels as well as outside on the terminals.

312    The installation of these systems and the general commissioning activities are considered in Chapter 12. However, there are specific electrical matters which are covered here, first the 21 kV system and then the OCS system.

### The 21 kV system

313    In addition to the major substations, there are numerous underground electrical rooms. The equipment in these all had to be electrically tested in due course. TLJV had further developed the electrical safety rules and eventually introduced rules which covered both the UK and French parts of the project. However, problems did occur mainly due to the distances (and therefore decreasing management control) in this project and also the increasing presence of sub-contractors who were often new to the site. TLJV addressed the problem of control at distance by instituting a procedure known as work authorisation documents (WADs) which is further described in Chapter 12. The second issue was addressed by insisting that all sub-contractors who worked on the electrical systems should be fully trained in the electrical safety rules.

314    Although this procedure generally worked, there were failures and on a number of occasions HSE found deficiencies which led to unsafe electrical practice. For example, a Prohibition Notice was served in February 1993 when inspectors saw an electrician working on a switchboard with exposed busbars and other electrical parts which were live at 400 V AC.

This occurred in one of the signalling rooms near to the UK crossover. HSE required that TLJV ensure compliance with the Electricity at Work Regulations 1989, which prevent work on live equipment unless proved necessary. Necessary work required further precautions, eg barriers, insulating mats and exclusion of non-test personnel. TLJV instituted further controls for their procedures after this.

315    Also, following several incidents of unauthorised personnel gaining access to electrical switch rooms, TLJV introduced a control system (the 'grey card' system taken from French electrical working practices) to control access. Non-electrical personnel who attended training in this system were permitted access to switch rooms for non-electrical work such as cleaning. They had to be in possession of a valid grey card.

316    A special area of control around the UK and French border at the mid-points of the marine tunnels had also to be instituted. One of the project electrical zones, known as Zone 8, spanned this boundary and there were several switch rooms on the UK side which received power from France. Procedures were implemented to ensure that the switch rooms were not inadvertently energised from France while work was being carried out in them. Concern over energisation of this zone had been expressed at an early stage as a result of two hazards: the potential paralleling of the UK and French national grids, and the loss of complete control over isolation by the UK side.

### The overhead catenary system (OCS)

317    Energisation of the OCS commenced in July 1993, with the final section through the middle of the tunnels being completed in early September. Both HSE and TLJV recognised the serious risk posed by energisation of the catenary in what was still a construction site employing several thousand people. In fact, TLJV had postponed the energisation of the OCS several times previously, partly on safety grounds.

318    TLJV's actions to minimise risk from the OCS, in the months leading up to energisation, included an extensive on-site publicity campaign to alert personnel to its hazards. Along with this, the contractors designated both running tunnels and areas of the terminal adjacent to the catenary as an 'orange card zone', to which access was strictly controlled via four access points, manned by security personnel. To enter this zone, personnel were required to have attended a safety training course and to produce a valid card. On several occasions after introduction of this procedure, due to changes in working practices, retraining and revalidation was required.

319    Operation of this orange card zone was generally successful, although there were several incidents including an occasion when inspectors saw two sub-contractors working on a ladder within the 3 m danger zone around the catenary and feeder wires at the UK crossover.

320    A potentially serious incident occurred in November 1993 when the 25 kV OCS was reconfigured for testing purposes. Normally the electrical supply to the OCS was separate to the two running tunnels. For the purposes of this test, one supply was taken from the terminal along the running tunnel north, through a mid-point connection and back along the running tunnel south to the UK terminal. The length of this circuit was approximately 44 km.

321    Prior to energisation, the catenary was inspected and a test zone area was set up in both running tunnels from which personnel were excluded. There was therefore no one at risk as the tunnels were physically closed off at cross-passages. However, when the system was energised, a ceramic post insulator supporting the feeder wire in running tunnel south failed explosively. This caused extensive arcing with the 5 kV catenary wire and associated tunnel metalwork, with the damage extending for approximately 300 m in both directions along the tunnel, on either side of the fault point. A small part of the feeder wire collapsed onto the tunnel floor.

322    TLJV had failed to re-set the protection relays to take into account the reduced fault current associated with doubling the length of the circuit. Therefore the fault persisted for two minutes until the appropriate circuit-breaker was opened manually. Because of the normal test zone exclusion there were no injuries.

323    Following the incident, TLJV revised the detection range of the relays to detect faults no matter how the system was configured. Procedures were also revised to ensure positive checks of relays were made prior to testing. This was one of a significant number of testing procedures, the others presenting no risk, but this example illustrates the need to take into account changed conditions which may arise from specialised tests.

**Summary of electrical health and safety matters**

- Design – high voltage electrical cabling needs to be of a standard to protect against fire. Equipment for areas where wet conditions are expected, especially on TBMs, needs to be to the required standard, particularly to mitigate against the risk of abnormal movement of machinery due to electrical short-circuit.

- Selection – a high standard of transformer is necessary; transformers containing mineral oils should not be used. Locomotives for underground railways can minimise fire and electrical short-circuit in wet and pollutant atmospheres.

- Use – deficiencies noted by personnel on electrical equipment should be immediately reported and rectified, and equipment damaged in use needs to be withdrawn from service. Power supplies to TBMs, particularly the process of disconnection and reconnection on extension of supplies, can be safely controlled by a permit-to-work system and written electrical procedures.

- Maintenance – it is important that electrical personnel are trained in underground and site conditions and follow written maintenance schedules.

- Repair – it is essential to ensure that the written electrical safety rules, procedures and permits are in force and are supported by management actions.

- Testing – electrical testing of installed permanent equipment is best controlled by written authorisation of work. In any system where overhead catenary is being tested, special attention has to be given to controlling risk for all people working in the area.

A train-mounted assembly scaffold for installation of tunnel services

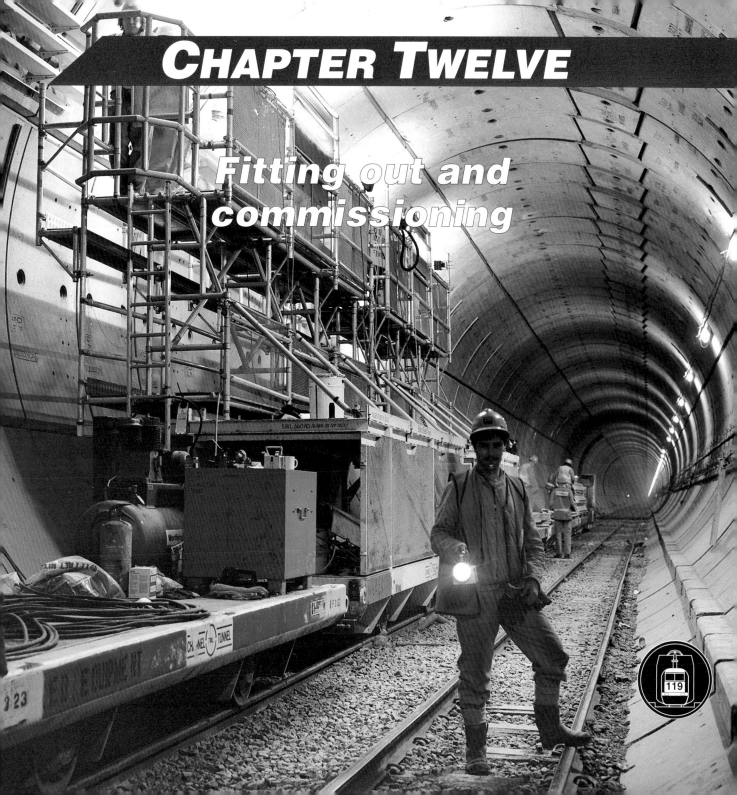

# CHAPTER TWELVE

## Fitting out and commissioning

## Introduction

324　During 1990, as the tunnelling drives progressed, work began on the installation of the final systems (the 'fixed equipment' activities) which would turn the project into an operational railway. Late in 1989, the land service tunnel had completed its drive and late in 1990 the two land running tunnels from Shakespeare Cliff to the terminal site at Folkestone broke through. In December 1990 the UK and French marine service tunnels met under the Channel. Initially it had been planned that all construction work would be completed by December 1992 with commissioning then taking place, followed by handover to the client, Eurotunnel, in June 1993. However there were considerable delays and towards the end of the project, parts of construction, fitting out and commissioning merged. The project was handed over to Eurotunnel in December 1993 but commissioning activities continued well into 1994.

325　This chapter describes the health and safety aspects of the fitting out and commissioning of the UK tunnels and terminal. The work involved in installing fixed equipment is briefly described followed by an examination of several important aspects of sub-contractors' work, ie working practices and equipment used, and communication and control.

326　The most important safety aspect of commissioning was that methods of control were exercised mainly by procedures such as the use of work authorisation documents, rule books, test procedures and restricted zones. TLJV and HSE learned much from the development of control systems during this time.

## Fitting out

327　The major work for fitting out the project was as follows:

(a)　Power and catenary (sub-contractor – Balfour Beatty Power Ltd): high voltage and low voltage electrical sub-stations (surface and tunnels):

　　(i)　power supply to lights, pumping stations, crossover, fan stations etc;

　　(ii)　overhead catenary to power the passenger and freight trains.

(b)　Mechanical systems (sub-contractor for linear systems – Laing Ltd):

　　(i)　linear systems – pipework for drainage, fire and cooling systems;

　　(ii)　non-linear systems – pumping stations and ventilation, piston relief duct;

(iii)  dampers and cross-passage and crossover doors.

(c)  Control and communications (sub-contractor – various including Sofrerail):

(i)  railway signalling system;

(ii)  data transmission;

(iii)  radio systems.

(d)  Trackwork (sub-contractor in tunnels – Channel Tunnel Trackwork Group):

(i)  concreting the invert in the two running tunnels (carried out by TLJV);

(ii)  laying and welding the rail tracks;

(iii)  second stage concreting of the rail track.

328  The numbers employed by the sub-contractors listed above, as well as numerous other sub-contractors, grew as the fixed equipment phase progressed. For example, in the quarter year April to June 1991, the average number employed by them was 1125; in October to December 1992 the average figure was 3760 (the highest number of sub-contractors). TLJV and the sub-contractors had a major task to ensure that these workers were given training in the individual working procedures of the companies concerned and also were familiar with the underground operations. Thus sub-contractors' employees went through induction both for tunnel operations and for the sub-contractors' working methods.

**Working practices and equipment**

329  Equipment in the service tunnel was fitted in the roof space. This included fire mains, cooling water pipes and electric cables. In the running tunnels, water pipes and electrical equipment were fitted around the axis or mid-point of the tunnel on the side opposite the cross-passages and the OCS was in the roof space. All this work was done by sub-contractors working off specially designed access platforms. In the service tunnel, until the invert was concreted during the latter part of 1992 and 1993, the work was performed off flatbed rail cars running on the construction gauge railway. The same procedure was used in the running tunnels until the standard gauge railway tracks were laid. After that time, standard gauge rail cars were provided with access platforms and in the end a substantial number (about 25) of standard gauge work trains operated daily in the running tunnels.

330    The specialist working platforms designed by the sub-contractors were often cantilevered to allow access and had standard edge protection with mesh infill. From time to time, employees of sub-contractors were seen working outside the confines of the purpose-built platforms and modifications had to be made. However, by and large these platforms allowed for safe access and provided a safe working place during the fixed equipment phase. The control measures adopted to prevent access within the 3 m danger zone of the live overhead catenary system when it was energised during 1993 are described in paragraph 318.

**Communication and control**

331    It is important to ensure good communication and control, particularly when the distances in the tunnels are long, and employees of different contractors are working in the same areas at the same time. The procedures adopted to control and communicate during the commissioning phase are described in paragraphs 340 to 355.

332    A major problem occurred during fitting out when, during a period of about six weeks in July and August 1992, employees from both France and the UK were working at the same time in part of the UK service tunnel. The UK contractors had driven the service tunnel an extra 4 km beyond the international border. When this drive was completed, a temporary border between the UK and France was located where the two drives had met. While the final 4 km of the UK service tunnel drive was legally in the UK, the running tunnels on either side, connected by cross-passages, were legally in France. This area was later referred to as the 'overlap zone'.

333    HSE inspectors visited this area in July 1992 and were seriously concerned about safety matters. In particular, radio communications had been removed between the sector and the UK Control Room, and French radio control had been installed. However, UK personnel could not make contact with the French radio control. A written procedure for a bilingual 'conductor' from the French contractors to travel with the UK trains was not being followed. The UK trains therefore had no communication with either control room, with consequent risk of collision. French trains also travelled on the tracks. In summary, there were four deficiencies in control and communication as follows:

(a)    UK trains were travelling in the overlap zone with no form of communication to anyone. There was a risk of collision with French trains, inability to discover where other work trains were located and the possible risk to French workers in the tunnel of being struck by a train.

(b)    Most of the French contractors working in the overlap zone were not wearing any form of high-visibility reflective clothing.

(c)    French work trains were travelling in this sector to two work locations. Although the UK contractors had provided look-outs at either end of their own trains when they were stopped, they could not communicate with the French train drivers.

(d)    There was evidence of smoking by the French contractors (the French contractors did not have a 'no smoking' rule in their tunnels).

334    These problems, discovered by HSE inspectors making a routine visit, resulted in all activities in the area being stopped until matters were rectified. HSE issued an Improvement Notice which required TLJV to make arrangements to ensure the safety at work of employees, their sub-contractors and the French sub-contractors by providing a safe system of work for the control of both train and personnel movements in the overlap zone.

335    The two parts of TML, both TLJV and TMC, the French contractors, reacted quickly and constructively to the issuing of the Improvement Notice. As well as carrying out the above actions, they set up emergency procedures and provided a bilingual engineer with the power to stop work. All personnel were trained in the procedures and were issued with badges indicating that they could work in the zone. A follow-up visit was paid by HSE inspectors accompanied by the French health and safety inspector (Inspector du Travail). This joint visit by two national inspectorates showed that the revised safety procedures were being observed by both UK and French contractors.

**Commissioning**

336    As the project moved towards completion in 1993, construction activities began to decline and the emphasis started to change to commissioning, that is, testing and proving all the systems for full operational use.

337    For the purposes of commissioning, the equipment in the tunnels was divided into primary 'systems', eg ventilation, rolling stock, overhead catenary system, which in turn were sub-divided into commissioning 'lots', eg the fire detection in the tunnel was divided into eight lots. The commissioning team carrying out this work was part of TLJV but had a different management team. However overall control rested with the senior management team led by the UK Operations Director. Site management had therefore to control commissioning fixed equipment installation and civil engineering work. The methods used are considered in paragraphs 340 to 355.

## Hazards of commissioning

338    Commissioning activities introduced a number of further hazards, in particular:

(a)    high-speed train movements in the running tunnels;

(b)    energisation of the 21 kV power supply system;

(c)    energisation of the 25 kV overhead catenary system;

(d)    mechanical hazards, eg cross-passage doors, crossover doors, pumping stations, ventilation.

339    Some of these hazards were described in Chapters 10 and 11. The management procedures used to control these hazards were work authorisation documents, rule books, test procedures and restricted and exclusion zones.

## Work authorisation documents

340    Throughout the commissioning phase, one of TLJV's principal objectives was to minimise conflict between activities. They sought to achieve this by:

(a)    separation of commissioning lots to prevent, eg inadvertent energisation of the OCS or activation of associated lots; and

(b)    the implementation of a complex work authorisation system known as work authorisation documents (WADs).

341    The WAD system was drawn up by TLJV, partly to overcome the considerable problems involved in controlling and co-ordinating commissioning activities and also in response to contractual requirements to provide Eurotunnel with a system suitable for controlling maintenance and service activities once commercial operation of the Fixed Link began.

342    In addition, commissioning had implications for safety not just on the UK side of the tunnel. A unified system was required which allowed both French and British parts of TML to be aware of and thus to prevent conflicting work activities in the other's part of the tunnel.

The WAD document was designed and used in the same form on both sides of the Channel, having been developed over a period of several months to ensure the exact translation of words and phrases. Someone wishing to carry out a work activity would request authorisation through the WAD office, providing all relevant details, ie location, work to be carried out, test procedures etc. Normally 48 hours notice was required, although for complex work this was extended to several weeks.

343    There was a single WAD office based at the terminal site which co-ordinated the issue of all such documents. Daily meetings were held at the WAD office, attended by the relevant managers with overall responsibility for designated areas. WAD applications were scrutinised and discussed to identify potential problems, hazards and conflict. Appropriate safety precautions were then stipulated in the WAD before it was granted, such as the need to follow a particular method statement.

344    TLJV's existing system of permits-to-work for a narrow range of particularly hazardous activities continued to operate and were identified as necessary precautions on the WAD. WADs were valid for a discrete period of time only. Prior to the start of work each day or shift, the work team leader would sign the WAD confirming that all safety precautions specified were in place. Failure to return the completed WAD to the WAD office, once work was finished, prevented further works in the area.

345    There were a number of initial problems with the WAD system:

(a)    In many cases the description of the work authorised by a particular WAD was extremely vague, eg 'LV/HV work in running tunnel' was a work description frequently used by a major sub-contractor, which effectively covered every conceivable electrical activity in the tunnels throughout this period. This made effective control of the work very difficult.

(b)    Inspectors found a number of instances where WADs had not been authorised by line management to indicate that the safety precautions were in place prior to work commencing. These WADs were invalid but work went on.

(c)    Some WADs were issued with vague or no safety precautions, such as 'treat all electrical equipment as live', when the WAD was for work on live electrical equipment.

(d)    WADs were designed to remain in the possession of the work team leader at the work site; in some instances WADs had to be handed over to security in exchange for keys to electrical rooms. The work team did not have copies, so it was difficult to check on compliance with the WAD and difficult for the employees to check they had implemented all the safety precautions.

346   However, the quality and implementation of the WAD system was good and improved noticeably as time went on. It was an effective tool to control and co-ordinate different work activities.

## Commissioning Rule Book

347   TLJV formulated detailed procedures with supplementary rules and instructions for the operation of the standard gauge railway prior to the introduction of the signalling system. Importantly, Section 9 of the Rule Book contained rules specifically concerned with safe working in the vicinity of the 25 kV OCS. Duties of key personnel were defined, together with the procedures to be followed for switching off electricity, emergency events, and work near to the overhead line equipment.

## Test procedures

348   Each commissioning activity had an associated test procedure drawn up by TLJV using information from plant suppliers and installers. Sequences of tests and checks for each piece of plant or system were detailed, along with specific safety procedures, frequently in the form of a check-list.

349   Examples of test procedures included those for commissioning of cross-passage and crossover doors. Commissioning and testing of the cross-passage doors located at each cross-passage junction between the service and running tunnels raised particular concern as a result of the trapping risk created when the doors open and close under power. Doubts had been raised as to the efficacy of the stop wires provided to minimise the crushing and trapping risk created both when the doors open and close under power. Each doorway weighs approximately 1500 kg and is driven open and closed by powerful electrical motors.

350   Inspectors observed the tests undertaken. The risks to commissioning engineers were well controlled, with all other personnel being excluded from the area. Following the commissioning test, the doors were electrically isolated.

351   Several potential hazards were identified at the large sliding doors at the crossover. These included shear points at the rear of the door in the opening cycle and a potential crushing risk as the doors met when closing. These doors were commissioned and tested under test zone conditions so that the area was demarcated and access restricted to test zone personnel only.

## Restricted zones

352    The use of 'orange cards' to restrict access to areas under the OCS is described in paragraph 318. The pre-energisation publicity, the training and the strict access arrangements were largely effective and there were no serious injuries or fatal accidents involving contact with the live overhead catenary while the system was under the control of the contractors.

## Exclusion zones

353    During two activities it was not possible to use procedures on their own and physical separation of the running tunnels was required where the hazards occurred. The activities were:

(a)    tests of the OCS (see Chapter 11, paragraphs 317 to 323);

(b)    high-speed train tests.

### *High-speed train tests*

354    Exclusion zones were used during high-speed train testing. As part of the commissioning programme, it was necessary to do a series of tests in the running tunnels with rolling stock operating at high speeds. The first of these in February 1993 was done to demonstrate the physical performance and properties of the OCS in running tunnel north. This test, known as the Mentor test, involved  diesel-drawn rolling stock and a special observation rail-car travelling at high speed. The OCS was not energised for this test.

355    In view of the high speeds of up to 160 kph, it was necessary to give careful consideration to safety matters. A detailed risk assessment was undertaken by the contractors identifying the precautions which would be required. These were discussed with HSE. Essentially, TLJV ceased work for the duration of the test and placed the running tunnel under strict control, with all cross-passages locked. In addition, people were stationed in the service tunnel to ensure that no one attempted to gain access. These people were provided with keys for use in the event of an emergency. The ventilation system in use at the time was switched off for the duration of the test. Ventilation at that time was a through flow system with air passing from the UK to France and so it was important to establish good co-ordination with regard to protection of the French site. TLJV confirmed that work would also cease in the French tunnels on the day of the test and that the French contractors had secured entry to their tunnels.

**Summary of health and safety matters during fitting out and commissioning**

● All sub-contractors received adequate safety induction into the tunnel environment and were provided with training with regard to fire and transport safety.

● Temporary support arrangements for fixed equipment, pipework, electrical equipment or rail track were designed and installed for safe support until permanent systems were installed.

● Arrangements need to be in place for communication and control of sub-contract activities, particularly those being carried out in the same area of tunnel. These should be agreed, understood, written down and monitored.

● Work authorisation documents provide a good method of health and safety control during fixed equipment and commissioning phases of projects.

● For particular activities, eg railways and electrical work, site rule books are appropriate. It is important that employees engaged in these activities are trained in accordance with the rule books.

● There were written test procedures which included safety arrangements for commissioning activities.

● Access needs to be restricted to areas of special risk and training provided on the nature of the restrictions as necessary. It is important that personnel are excluded from certain areas during commissioning, eg during high-speed vehicle movements or special testing of electrical systems.

# APPENDIX ONE

## *Historical background*

1    The earliest proposals for the construction of a Channel tunnel were put forward in France in 1802 and 1803 for an excavated tunnel to provide a road for horse-drawn carriages, or for a submerged tube. Neither of these schemes got anywhere and the idea lay dormant until 1833 when a young French engineer Aimé Thomé de Gamond became interested. He spent more than 30 years in the mid-19th century promoting various schemes to establish a fixed link and conducted his own rudimentary but systematic surveys of the Channel by diving to the sea bed weighted by four bags of flints; his return to the surface was aided by ten inflated pigs' bladders. During one dive to around 100 feet he was attacked by conger eels but 'was fortunate enough not to open my mouth'.

2    De Gamond's ideas were taken up by an English engineer, William Low, who was the first to put forward the idea of a pair of tunnels each containing a single rail track and connected by cross-passages. The support of both the French and British governments for these proposals was eventually obtained and in 1872, a Channel Tunnel Company was set up in England, followed by one in France. A large amount of surveying work took place in 1875–76 but the schemes of the original Channel Tunnel Company came to nothing.

3    Sir Edward Watkin was the Chairman of the South Eastern Railway Company, which owned land along the railway line between Folkestone and Dover. In 1880 his engineers sank a 74 ft deep shaft at Abbots Cliff, and drove a horizontal pilot tunnel, with the aim of constructing a Channel tunnel connecting with the coastal rail line. He then formed the Submarine Continental Railway Company, and also reached an understanding with the French Channel Tunnel Company.

4    A second shaft was then sunk from a small level shelf of ground at the foot of Shakespeare Cliff, which was also the location for the shaft of the Dover Colliery. A 7 ft diameter pilot tunnel was bored roughly in the direction of the end of the Admiralty Pier at Dover and by February 1882 the tunnel was about two thirds of a mile long. However, in April 1882 the Board of Trade instructed that boring operations be suspended because of British fears of invasion.

5     The tunnel had been bored by a tunnelling machine designed by Colonel Frederick Beaumont and was the forerunner of modern tunnel boring machines. It was powered by compressed air and the tunnel was unlined. Beaumont's tunnel crosses the line of the existing tunnels and was entered briefly by TLJV staff when the modern TBMs passed through it.

6     Unsuccessful proposals for a tunnel were made in the early 1960s but, towards the end of that decade, both governments finally agreed and the project got properly underway in the early 1970s. The UK pulled out of the project around 1975 and the scheme was abandoned, but not before significant progress had been made

7      On the UK side the tunnels created (the access tunnel built from the upper Shakespeare Cliff site to the lower site and the adit driven downwards to the line and level of the tunnel workings together with the 300 m of service tunnel which had been driven towards France) were later incorporated into the present Fixed Link. This section of tunnel is now part of the marine service tunnel even though it is only 4.5 m in diameter compared with the 4.8 m diameter of the rest of the service tunnel.

8      Following an 'Invitation to Promoters' in April 1985, the Governments of the French Republic and the United Kingdom selected the scheme put forward jointly by the Channel Tunnel Group and France Manche (the Eurotunnel companies), to construct and operate a Fixed Link of twin rail tunnels connected by a service tunnel. The Governments then signed the Treaty of Canterbury in February 1986 and a Concession Agreement with the two companies in March 1986. Eurotunnel in turn signed a construction contract with the ten companies forming Transmanche Link in August 1986.

9      The Treaty set out the broad framework within which the two states would co-operate over the supervision of the Fixed Link, and established an Intergovernmental Commission (IGC) 'to supervise, in the name of the two Governments, all matters concerning the construction and operation of the Fixed Link.' It also established a Safety Authority (SA) 'to advise and assist the IGC on all matters concerning safety in the construction and operation of the Fixed Link.'

10     The Concession Agreement established the rights and obligations of the concessionaires to develop, finance, construct and operate the Fixed Link. The Treaty and Concession Agreement were implemented in UK law by the Channel Tunnel Act 1987, section 10(1) which extended the law of England, including the Health and Safety at Work etc Act 1974 (HSW Act), as far as the new frontier with France.

# APPENDIX TWO

# *Control of smoke by the ventilation system*

This appendix describes the various computer fire modelling work carried out by both HSE and Cambridge Environmental Research Consultants (CERC).

1  Prior to breakthrough of the UK and French marine service tunnels in December 1990 the UK marine service tunnel was a long blind heading (at one time in excess of 20 km) and the substantial fire risk posed by the storage and use of mineral oil in the TBMs (see Chapter 4) prompted HSE's first computer fire modelling work for the project. Under the direction of HSE's research laboratory, this fire model (the NEAR FIRE model) was refined by CERC, a commercial consultancy affiliated to Cambridge University and contracted to TLJV. The results indicated that initial smoke velocities in the tunnel might exceed the speed at which workers could escape on foot from a fire. The results were used in the development of fire precautions which are described in Chapter 4.

2  The consequences of small fires in other parts of the blind heading were modelled using the TBM mineral oil risk assessment report. The fires were considered as equivalent to small open trays of mineral oil and the consequences determined. The work suggested that the fire smoke and hot gases would not be extensive, moving less than 100 m from the source, and that the fire could be readily extinguished with hand-held equipment.

## Post-breakthrough controls

3  With further development of the tunnels, and following breakthrough, significant changes were made to the ventilation system to full-face tunnel ventilation driven by a mid-point fan station, and physical smoke separation at both cross-passages and piston relief ducts increasingly became impracticable.

4  Consequently the NEAR FIRE model previously developed for TBMs no longer matched the changing circumstances. This model only provided information on pollution within the immediate vicinity of the seat of the fire. For the first time tunnel-wide information was needed on how fire pollutants would move between tunnels and, more importantly, how these events could be controlled by management of the ventilation system. HSE advised that the proposed computational fluid dynamic approach was too complex for this purpose and recommended some tried and tested ventilation packages

5    The US Bureau of Mines ventilation model, M FIRE, was chosen to provide an overall model to predict the pollutant contamination from a fire and to establish how operation of the ventilation system affected the spread of pollutants. The resultant HSE NEAR FIRE/M FIRE model (known as the HSE/M FIRE model) was developed by CERC.

**Initial modelling work**

6    CERC explored the predicted air movements between the tunnels via cross-passages (CPs) and piston relief ducts (PRDs) on the UK side of the project. The results showed that when the ventilation in each constituent tunnel was in balance, doubling or halving airway resistance produced little inter-tunnel air movement. It soon became apparent that this would be the case for all but the most serious of blockages in the main tunnels. As anticipated, the model demonstrated that for a balanced tunnel ventilation system, the air would move down the principal tunnels rather than divert, or interchange, through CPs and PRDs.

7    The model also showed that air movement would take place between adjacent tunnels where pressure imbalances existed in the system, such as the crossover and the mid-point fan station.

**Subsequent modelling work**

8    In fire modelling work, the size of the fire being investigated is critical. A fire can be seen as a form of heat pump: it draws in fresh air, causes chemical and physical rearrangements, and generates a large volume of smoke and hot gases. In certain circumstances these hot gases are at a sufficient volume and pressure to override or redirect local ventilation. Extensive modelling work using the HSE/M FIRE programme was undertaken. During 1991 CERC worked on validation of TLJV's proposed ventilation actions and escape routings in the event of a fire emergency in the UK marine tunnels.

9    The modelling work undertaken considered not only 1, 5, 10 and 20 MW fires at various locations in the tunnel complex, but also the effect on the fire of being located in between CPs and PRDs or directly alongside these tunnel features and consequently the effect on the spread of smoke between tunnels. These estimated fire size figures, provided by HSE, were based on the likely output from ignition of a pool of diesel fuel, the volume of which was based on the full inventory of the locomotives in use.

10    CERC modelled the consequences of fires at five locations, chosen for their proximity to areas where pressure imbalances might occur, namely the pit bottom area, the crossover and the three mid-point fan stations. These were considered to be the worst case scenarios. CERC drew the following conclusions:

(a)     For the UK marine tunnels, at least one tunnel remained sufficiently free from the products of combustion to serve both as a means of escape and a route for rescue. In spite of some minor discrepancies this agreed with TLJV's proposed ventilation actions and escape routings shown in their fire response diagram (FRD).

(b)     A fire in the UK land tunnels would not contaminate the UK marine tunnels (and afterwards the French tunnels) if the mid-point fans were shut down.

(c)     On the French side of the mid-point fans, at the time largely French occupied, contamination from the modelled fires would leave at least one tunnel capable of serving both as a means of escape and a route for rescue.

11     The situation at the French crossover was more problematical, because further along the tunnel from this crossover all tunnels would have became smoke-logged to some extent. However, this was not a serious problem as a result of the large amount of time taken for contamination to reach the French workings.

12     While outputs of contamination for the fire location scenarios which were modelled largely confirmed TLJV's intended escape routing, as described in their FRDs, pressure imbalances in the system leading to cross-contamination between tunnels were identified. With this knowledge, the contractors were able to address these problem areas either in terms of hardware, to detect a fire at an early stage so that the mid-point fans could quickly be shut down to limit the spread of contamination, or to consider the re-routing of personnel at the time of an incident around the crossover via the service tunnel.

13     One feature of the model is that its output is in terms of percent total contamination; that is, it does not specify the components of the contamination. HSE addressed this shortcoming by calculating output from a 10 MW diesel fire in terms of the concentration in parts per million of the main contaminants: smoke, carbon monoxide and carbon dioxide. In addition, the concentration of these contaminants depends upon the quantity of fire ventilation, so two values were calculated; the lower value corresponded to a stoichiometric combustion (close to ideal conditions where the amount of oxygen used is just enough to give complete oxidation to the most stable oxide in the fuel), while upper values corresponded to burning in poorly ventilated conditions.

## Accuracy of the model

14    Fundamental to HSE's acceptance of the use of the ventilation system to control smoke underground was the accuracy of the modelling work. This was established in a number of ways. The NEAR FIRE model was largely consistent with the results from some real tunnel fire tests undertaken at HSE's research laboratory and the ventilation model (M FIRE) is well tried and tested in the mining field. Further, the data collected by TLJV's comprehensive telemetry system following an incident in the land running tunnel at Holywell on 23 and 24 August 1991, was used by CERC for comparison with data output from the modelling procedure.

15    The incident occurred when the activated charcoal filter of an exhaust treatment unit attached to a diesel generator caught fire. Large amounts of carbon monoxide were produced which spread throughout the tunnels, giving rise to significant levels of carbon monoxide there. The laboratory provided an estimate of the likely pollutant levels in each of the relevant airways as the incident progressed. Because the fire was not the same type described by the NEAR FIRE model, notably in terms of the variation of the fire size over time, a mean figure was used for the heat output. The comparison between actual and predicted figures was, however, good and gave qualified confidence in the use of the modelling procedure. The concentration of contaminants along each tunnel predicted by the model was reproduced fairly well, both in terms of the timing of changes and the values themselves. The predicted transfer of contaminants between tunnels also correlated well.

16    In the same report, CERC also described further modelling on out of balance mid-point fans and reduced mid-point fans, and they considered further scenarios including fires larger than 10 MW. This work arose from the fact that, from time to time, the ventilation fans had to be taken out of service. Should a fire have occurred at this time, TLJV would have needed to rebalance the ventilation system to minimise any air movement between tunnels.

## Latter stages of the project

17    As the project progressed into the mechanical and electrical phase, the ventilation system was further modified by removal of the Holywell and mid-point fan stations. The supplementary ventilation system (SVS) fans which comprise part of the permanent installation were utilised from December 1992 to provide a bi-directional ventilation system by drawing air into the pit bottom area which then flowed both towards France and towards the UK portal. All the air from the SVS system was introduced into the tunnels via adit A2 and therefore regulators had to be placed in each of the land tunnels to ensure that a balanced ventilation system was maintained. Revised fire response diagrams (FRD – see Chapter 6) and rescue

procedures were formulated by TLJV. Much of the existing modelling work was relevant to this new system although interchange of air between the tunnels in the pit bottom area inevitably occurred. TLJV used the mines ventilation VENT 4 model to predict these air flows.

18    The ventilation system was subject to several further changes, although the principle of maintaining balanced air flows in the tunnels remained.

# APPENDIX THREE

# *Accident and employment statistics*

**Employment statistics**

1      Numbers employed on the project by all contractors are listed per quarter from April 1988 until December 1993 in the sixth column of Table 1. These figures were provided by TLJV to HSE. No figures are available before April 1988, when HSE began to collate this information, or after December 1993, when TLJV handed control of the sites to Eurotunnel.

2      Table 2, which commences in April 1991, distinguishes between overall numbers employed on the sites and numbers of sub-contractors. These are listed under the titles 'All workers' and 'Sub-contractors'.

**Accident statistics**

3      Table 1 lists numbers of injuries (columns 2 to 5) and incidence rates (columns 7 and 8) for the project from April 1988 to December 1993.

4      Table 2 provides more detailed information about accident rates to sub-contractors.

5      Tables 3 and 4 show twelve month moving averages for injuries from April 1988 to December 1993.

6      No comparison is made between these figures and accident figures reported from other parts of the construction industry. HSE have confidence of almost 100% reporting for Channel Tunnel accident figures, and estimate a significantly lower reporting rate for general construction industry figures.

7      No comparison is made here between UK figures and French site figures. Statutory reporting requirements, calculation of accident rates and measurement of manpower on the project differed between the two sites, making any such comparison difficult (but see Chapter 1).

**Table 1**   Injuries at the Channel Tunnel reported to HSE's Factory and Agricultural Inspectorates

| Date of accident | Number of injuries | | | | Employment | Incidence rates* | |
|---|---|---|---|---|---|---|---|
| | Fatal | Major | Over 3 day | Total | Data | Fatal & major | All reported |
| **1988/89** | | | | | | | |
| April - June 1988 | - | 6 | 29 | 35 | 3015.3 | 199.0 | 1160.7 |
| July - Sept 1988 | - | 3 | 35 | 38 | 3937.7 | 76.2 | 965.0 |
| Oct - Dec 1988 | - | 5 | 26 | 31 | 4821.0 | 103.7 | 643.0 |
| Jan - March 1989 | 2 | 7 | 46 | 55 | 5395.0 | 166.8 | 1019.5 |
| **Total 1988/89** | 2 | 21 | 136 | 159 | 4292.3 | 535.8 | 3704.3 |
| **1989/90** | | | | | | | |
| April - June 1989 | - | 9 | 35 | 44 | 5949.0 | 151.3 | 739.6 |
| July - Sept 1989 | - | 11 | 59 | 70 | 6578.0 | 167.2 | 1064.2 |
| Oct - Dec 1989 | 1 | 18 | 71 | 90 | 6996.3 | 271.6 | 1286.4 |
| Jan - March 1990 | 1 | 9 | 91 | 101 | 7602.3 | 131.5 | 1328.5 |
| **Total 1989/90** | 2 | 47 | 256 | 305 | 6781.4 | 722.6 | 4497.6 |
| **1990/91** | | | | | | | |
| April - June 1990 | 2 | 16 | 86 | 104 | 8320.0 | 216.3 | 1250.0 |
| July - Sept 1990 | 1 | 9 | 68 | 78 | 7931.7 | 126.1 | 983.4 |
| Oct - Dec 1990 | - | 3 | 100 | 103 | 7536.0 | 39.8 | 1366.8 |
| Jan - March 1991 | - | 7 | 103 | 110 | 7759.3 | 90.2 | 1417.7 |
| **Total 1990/91** | 3 | 35 | 357 | 395 | 7886.9 | 481.8 | 5008.3 |
| **1991/92** | | | | | | | |
| April - June 1991 | - | 11 | 71 | 82 | 7781.0 | 141.4 | 1053.8 |
| July - Sept 1991 | - | 11 | 81 | 92 | 7570.0 | 145.3 | 1215.3 |
| Oct - Dec 1991 | - | 9 | 55 | 64 | 7371.0 | 122.1 | 868.3 |
| Jan - March 1992 | - | 2 | 64 | 66 | 6851.3 | 29.2 | 963.3 |
| **Total 1991/92** | - | 33 | 271 | 304 | 7393.3 | 446.4 | 4111.8 |
| **1992/93** | | | | | | | |
| April - June 1992 | - | 6 | 71 | 77 | 6383.7 | 94.0 | 1206.2 |
| July - Sept 1992 | - | 8 | 35 | 43 | 6081.0 | 131.6 | 707.1 |
| Oct - Dec 1992 | 1 | 9 | 40 | 50 | 5995.3 | 166.8 | 834.0 |
| Jan - March 1993 | - | 5 | 30 | 35 | 5209.4 | 96.0 | 671.9 |
| **Total 1992/93** | 1 | 28 | 176 | 205 | 5917.4 | 490.1 | 3464.4 |
| **1993/94** | | | | | | | |
| April - June 1993 | - | - | 9 | 9 | 3479.3 | - | 258.7 |
| July - Sept 1993 | - | 1 | 8 | 9 | 2661.7 | 37.6 | 338.1 |
| Oct - Dec 1993 | - | 1 | 1 | 2 | 1942.0 | 51.5 | 103.0 |

* Rates per 100 000 workers/sub-contractors
Source: HSE Channel Tunnel Accident Database

138

**Table 2**   Injuries at the Channel Tunnel reported to HSE's Factory and Agricultural Inspectorates

| Date of accident | Number of injuries | | | | Employment Data | Incidence rates* | |
|---|---|---|---|---|---|---|---|
| | Fatal | Major | Over 3 day | Total | | Fatal & major | All reported |
| **ALL WORKERS** | | | | | | | |
| April - June 1991 | - | 11 | 71 | 82 | 7781.0 | 141.4 | 1053.8 |
| July - Sept 1991 | - | 11 | 81 | 92 | 7570.0 | 145.3 | 1215.3 |
| Oct - Dec 1991 | - | 9 | 55 | 64 | 7371.0 | 122.1 | 868.3 |
| Jan - March 1992 | - | 2 | 64 | 66 | 6851.3 | 29.2 | 963.3 |
| **Total 1991/92** | - | 33 | 271 | 304 | 7393.3 | 446.4 | 4111.8 |
| April - June 1992 | - | 6 | 71 | 77 | 6383.7 | 94.0 | 1206.2 |
| July - Sept 1992 | - | 8 | 35 | 43 | 6081.0 | 131.6 | 707.1 |
| Oct - Dec 1992 | 1 | 9 | 40 | 50 | 5995.3 | 166.8 | 834.0 |
| Jan - March 1993 | - | 5 | 30 | 35 | 5209.4 | 96.0 | 671.9 |
| **Total 1992/93** | 1 | 28 | 176 | 205 | 5917.4 | 490.1 | 3464.4 |
| April - June 1993 | - | - | 9 | 9 | 3479.3 | - | 258.7 |
| July - Sept 1993 | - | 1 | 8 | 9 | 2661.7 | 37.6 | 338.1 |
| Oct - Dec 1993 | - | 1 | 1 | 2 | 1942.0 | 51.5 | 103.0 |
| **SUB-CONTRACTORS** | | | | | | | |
| April - June 1991 | - | 1 | 11 | 12 | 1175.0 | 85.1 | 1021.3 |
| July - Sept 1991 | - | 4 | 22 | 26 | 1973.0 | 202.7 | 1317.8 |
| Oct - Dec 1991 | - | 3 | 24 | 27 | 2694.0 | 111.4 | 965.1 |
| Jan - March 1992 | - | 1 | 28 | 29 | 2959.0 | 33.8 | 98.0 |
| **Total 1991/92** | - | 9 | 85 | 94 | 2200.3 | 409.0 | 4272.1 |
| April - June 1992 | - | 5 | 48 | 53 | 3074.7 | 164.1 | 1739.0 |
| July - Sept 1992 | - | 5 | 22 | 27 | 3471.3 | 144.0 | 777.8 |
| Oct - Dec 1992 | - | 7 | 22 | 29 | 3760.7 | 186.1 | 771.1 |
| Jan - March 1993 | - | 2 | 13 | 15 | 2891.7 | 69.2 | 518.7 |
| **Total 1992/93** | - | 19 | 105 | 124 | 3292.9 | 577.0 | 3765.7 |
| April - June 1993 | - | - | 4 | 4 | 1910.3 | - | 209.4 |
| July - Sept 1993 | - | - | 3 | 3 | 1605.0 | - | 186.9 |
| Oct - Dec 1993 | - | - | 1 | 1 | 1146.3 | - | 87.2 |

\*    Rates per 100 000 workers/sub-contractors
Source: HSE Channel Tunnel Accident Database

139

**Table 3**   Channel Tunnel injury incidence rates (Twelve month moving averages – all
reported injuries)

Incidence rate

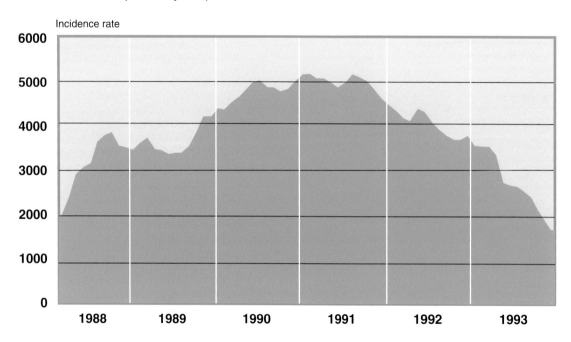

Rates per 100 000 workers

**Table 4**  Channel Tunnel injury incidence rates (Twelve month moving averages –
fatal and major injuries)

Incidence rate

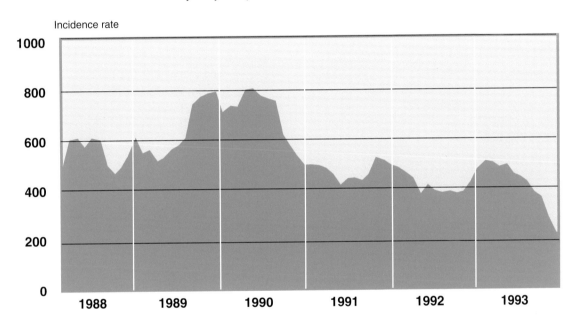

Rates per 100 000 workers

# GLOSSARY

**Adit** – the inclined access tunnels to the underground workings at Shakespeare Cliff (adit A1 and adit A2).

**Control Centre** – the communications and emergency control rooms at Shakespeare Cliff.

**Crossover** – the UK marine cavern approximately 7 km out undersea from Shakespeare Cliff.

**Eurotunnel** – the client company who own and operate the passenger railway.

**Fire loading** – the amount of combustible material in the plant, equipment and materials used in the tunnels.

**Inundation** – accidental substantial ingress of sea water.

**Invert** – the lowest part of the inside of a tunnel.

**Land running tunnel north/south** – the northerly/southerly railway tunnels between the UK terminal and Shakespeare Cliff (7.6 m diameter).

**Leaky feeder aerial/radio system** – an underground radio system relying on a linear aerial passing along the tunnel.

**Marine running tunnel north/south** – the northerly/southerly railway tunnels under the Channel (7.6 m diameter).

**Overhead catenary system (OCS)** – the 25 kV power supply for operational passenger trains. The wires for the OCS are located in the roof of each of the running tunnels as well as outside on the terminals.

**Service tunnel (land/marine)** – the 4.8 m diameter service tunnel between the running tunnels.

**Shakespeare Cliff site** – the main UK tunnel construction site until 1992 (upper site was at the cliff top and housed offices etc, lower site was the outside construction storage area at the base of the cliff with adits A1 and A2).

**TLJV** – Translink Joint Venture (UK construction consortium).

**TML** – Transmanche Link, the ten UK and French construction companies who carried out the work.

**TMC** – Transmanche Construction, the French construction consortium.

**UK terminal** – the railway terminal near Folkestone.

Printed in the UK for the Health and Safety Executive C30  5/96